D1347561

LSD, Man & Society

FRANK BARRON

NEIL CHAYET

NICHOLAS J. GIARMAN

MURRAY E. JARVIK

MILTON H. JOFFE

ALBERT A. KURLAND

DONALD B. LOURIA

WALTER N. PAHNKE

DOMINICK P. PURPURA

LSD, MAN & SOCIETY

Edited by Richard C. DeBold
and Russell C. Leaf

Wesleyan University Press

MIDDLETOWN, CONNECTICUT

Copyright © 1967 by Wesleyan University

BF 209
.L9 L2

INDIANA
UNIVERSITY
LIBRARY

NORTHWEST

ISBN: 0-8195-3079-4
Library of Congress Catalog Number: 67-24111
Manufactured in the United States of America
First printing October 1967; second printing December 1967
third printing April 1968; fourth printing September 1970

Contents

Introduction

We need a sober assessment of what we know about LSD—what we know confidently, what we know less than confidently and what we do not know at all. And we need to secure this information in terms that the intelligent layman can understand.

BURTON C. HALLOWELL
Executive Vice President, Wesleyan University

MR. HALLOWELL'S words are from his introductory remarks on the occasion at which the papers contained in this book were given, a public symposium held in the Wesleyan University chapel in March of 1967. They reflect the intentions of the editors and of the speakers. We set out to discover what was known about LSD, and beyond LSD itself, about the people who use it and the society in which it has become a powerful agent of concern. There can be no doubt of the impact of LSD. In fact, we were so sure of general acquaintance with it that we did not feel it necessary to begin with a description of LSD or of the way in which it is used, although we did include such descriptions later. Most people who pick up this book will be aware of LSD, and they will have some knowledge of what it does and what it is reputed to do. As several of our contributors point out, the press and popular magazines have devoted a great deal of space and time to popularization of the folklore of LSD. But folklore is far from enough. If society and individuals are to cope with the effects of LSD and other such materials, we need facts of a usable nature.

This book begins with a discussion of the relationship between the individual and LSD—the why, the how and the abuse. Frank Barron, who has written at length on the subject of creativity, opens the discussion by tackling the difficult problem of the motivations that lead people to use LSD. Investigations of the motivations that impel people to behave in certain ways are highly difficult to carry out successfully, perhaps because people often report their motives with poor insight into themselves. But Barron is in a unique position to succeed, as he is a staff-member of the Institute of Personality Assessment and Research at the

University of California in Berkeley and has ready access to "the action" in the San Francisco Bay area. As his article shows, he is an astute observer and a clear interpreter. He begins with an assessment of the historical factors that have led to the present *uncommitted* nature of some young people. From his study he develops his main theme, which is that the stance adopted by many takers of LSD is a form of social protest. As he evolves his typology of LSD usage, Barron returns again and again to that theme; and in the discussions that followed the presentation of the papers clear evidence that he has made a valid point does emerge. Much of the discussion revolves about the dissatisfaction of people with present American society.

But the psychomimetic drugs are not necessarily instruments of protest against society, nor are they necessarily anti-societal agents. In their paper, Dr. Kurland and his co-workers present a positive view of the potential of LSD as a servant of man and society. The paper is a progress report on a major research enterprise in which patients at a state hospital have been treated by use of LSD. The results of the treatment proved to be highly successful, given intensive preparation of the patients before LSD was used. Again and again in his discussion, Kurland makes the point that LSD can be a beneficial tool in certain situations if it is used by trained medical personnel, who are expert in the preparation of the persons receiving the drug. Included in his paper are lengthy direct reports by the patients themselves. This is the sort of evidence that can be either highly convincing and strongly veridical or badly misleading and subject to criticism. Kurland imbeds the reports in a careful evaluation of the evidence and cautious speculation about the future. There can be no doubt of his and his co-workers' concern for the scientific aspects of their work and for the need for careful evaluation of the therapeutic potential of LSD.

Lest we read Kurland's hopeful, yet cautious appraisal of the possibilities of LSD without an awareness of its dangers, the paper by Dr. Louria that follows speaks directly to the matter of the abuse of LSD. Louria, who has engaged in a number of public debates over uncontrolled usage of LSD, conveys his deep concern that the pleasure-to-risk ratio is far too high in the case of LSD. In his presentation he gives data to support his arguments.

Collected at Bellevue Hospital in New York City, his evidence shows that there have been a large number of cases of people admitted to the hospital after using LSD. In the paper, Louria breaks down the cases by occupation and interprets the data as strong support for prohibition of LSD by law. Perhaps the best way to express Louria's position is to say that he feels that control is necessary until careful medical research has provided insight into the dangers and risks that LSD involves. His presentation is charged with his sincerity and concern for the individual, and his arguments drive directly to his point: the pleasure-to-risk ratio must be taken into account.

Following Louria's paper, we include discussion from the audience. Perhaps the greatest insight into the concerns of both students and laymen can be gathered from these discussions. The discussion following the first three papers actually took place in the afternoon and thus came after the discussions appearing later in the book. The reader will have little difficulty because of this arrangement, since the discussions were quite autonomous.

The next three papers are concerned with the impact of LSD on society. The first of the series, by Dr. Pahnke, is an exploration of the possibility that LSD has profound religious significance for those who use it. As an examination of his credentials will show, Pahnke is perhaps uniquely prepared to tackle this difficult and highly controversial business. He holds an M.D and a Ph.D., both from Harvard. He is a psychiatrist and a theologian. Impressive in its reliance on data in these matters, the emergent conclusion of Pahnke's paper is that a profound change in experience, such as that following the use of LSD, can result in a radical alteration of a person's view of life. But the paper is far more than a testimonial or a speculation. As a scientist and a scholar, Pahnke has gathered a good deal of evidence, which he discusses. He presents both frequency data from controlled experiments and reports from his subjects. These reports are particularly graphic, as are those of Kurland. Just as Kurland did, Pahnke expresses deep concern that LSD be used only by those who are very carefully trained and that it be administered only to fully prepared recipients.

However much LSD may seem a possible boon or threat to society, it is surely a drug, and as such it is of direct concern to those regulatory agencies of the government charged with drug control. The most important of these agencies is the Federal Food and Drug Administration, with which Milton Joffe is associated. In his paper, Joffe presents an appraisal of the problem of LSD as it appears from the standpoint of a governmental agency responsible to society for regulation of the drug. He examines such aspects as the steps being taken by the federal government to locate the illicit sources of the drug, the effective size of the problem, the analysis of samples of the illicit drug and the programs of research on LSD that are being sponsored by his agency. As in earlier papers, Joffe makes a firm plea for continued research into the nature and effects of LSD and suggests methods for the sponsorship of such research.

The final paper in the section on society and LSD presents an analysis of the existing law related to the use of LSD. Neil Chayet is particularly well qualified to discuss the legal aspects of drug usage. He is an assistant professor at the Law–Medicine Institute of Boston University and specializes in the legal aspects of medical problems. With wit and clarity he ranges over the ordinances that are already on the books and those in the mill that relate to the problems of LSD. It is these laws that are the effective instruments of social control. But Chayet takes some pains to point out that much of the process of law is by precedent, and he discusses some of the precedents relating to LSD and its use.

At this point in the book we present the evening discussion that followed the preceding three papers. The discussion lasted officially until 11:30 p.m. At that point the moderator was exhausted and called a halt to things. But the audience stayed on, without a recorder, until 2:30 the following morning, discussing further the matters contained in the recorded session. Unfortunately, some of the most poignant remarks from the audience were not clearly understood. We have tried our best to be complete and accurate. The results speak for themselves. The social and interpersonal concerns expressed are a tribute to the people who came to the sessions and who had the courage and strength to speak out.

The last section of the book concerns the biological effects of LSD. Actually, these were the first three papers given at the symposium, but we present them last here, because they are somewhat technical and we do not wish to inhibit people from reading the other papers by finding the biological presentations somewhat difficult. Each of the speakers did a fine job of handling his material in a way that an interested layman can manage to understand. Of course, no book on LSD would be truly complete without an examination of these matters. We are convinced that those who are most interested in LSD, either from personal or from societal concerns, will ask what LSD is doing to the biology of the individual, a question that these papers answer in terms of the latest research on pharmacology and neurophysiological action and behavior.

This section begins with a discussion by Nicholas Giarman of the diverse pharmacological actions of LSD. Professor Giarman and his colleagues have been concerned in their own investigations with understanding the biochemical mechanism of the powerful behavioral actions of LSD. He describes the physical structure and chemistry of LSD, its potency and duration of action, its pharmacological effects on various biological systems and its metabolism. He takes up biochemical theories of the possible mode of action of LSD, as well as of a variety of other agents that are pharmacologically, but not chemically, similar to LSD.

Dr. Dominick Purpura was one of the first investigators to attempt to discover where and how LSD acts on the functioning of the brain. He discusses the neuroanatomical and neurophysiological mechanisms that are likely to be involved in its actions, and he explains how our understanding of LSD's actions has been a function of our incomplete, but growing knowledge about how the brain controls behavior.

The third paper, by Dr. Murray E. Jarvik, reviews laboratory investigations of the effects of LSD on behavior. Jarvik's own investigations of LSD in laboratory situations began at the time when he had just completed his academic studies for his M.D. and for his Ph.D. in psychology. The extensive work that he and his colleagues carried out in animals and man, beginning in 1952, prepared the ground for our present approaches to laboratory investigation of LSD. They did not lead him to expect our present social problems, however, as he points out. Like Giarman and Purpura, Jarvik is very concerned with the need for a great deal of further research on LSD under controlled circumstances in order to provide better answers to the pressing questions about its safety and value.

The discussion following these biological papers made clear that the audience was also deeply concerned about the biological and psychological safety of LSD usage. Definitive answers to the questions posed by this concern are often not available and in some areas, unfortunately, are not even being sought.

The book, then, forms a tripartite unit that reflects our understanding of an important societal concern: the biology of LSD, the relationship of LSD to the individual and the relationship of LSD to society. We believe that these papers will be an invaluable aid to all those who really want to know about LSD, such people as practicing doctors, college and high-school counselors, parents and individuals who are asking the questions: who, why, with what effect? The papers are very readable, make a sincere attempt to present fact and avoid folklore and cover the various aspects of the problem. The speakers, as well as the members of the audience who freely gave of themselves in discussion, have made a contribution to the solution of a serious problem.

Books such as the present one do not come into being without a great deal of work and support by people whose names do not appear on the title page. In the present case, the editors and moderators, Richard C. DeBold and Russell C. Leaf,* are deeply grateful to Dr. Albert Pawlowski of the Small Grants Section of the National Institutes of Mental Health. Not only did he handle our request for funds to defray expenses of the symposium, but he was also present and helped during that grueling day. The N. I. M. H., through Grant *MH 13798,* provided financial support and made the conference possible. At Wesleyan University, Robert A. Rosenbaum, the provost, and Burton C. Hallowell, then executive vice-president, provided encouragement and resources. Besides these a number of students and faculty lent willing hands during the conference. We are truly appreciative.

RICHARD C. DEBOLD
RUSSELL C. LEAF

Middletown, Connecticut

* Mr. Leaf's contributions to organizing, moderating and editing this symposium were partly supported by United States Public Health Service Grant *MH 13261–01.*

LSD, Man & Society

1   Motivational Patterns in LSD Usage*

By FRANK BARRON

WHY on earth would a drug that profoundly affects consciousness and the efficiency of mental functioning in ways that are difficult to predict and that are potentially dangerous to the person who uses it become popular, especially among the young, the well educated and those who are well chanced in life? What are the motives for its use? This is the question to which I address myself in this paper.

It would be easy enough to rest upon the observation that the chemical substance most instrumental in the spread of the psychedelic movement is printer's ink. Whatever else may be true about LSD, there is no doubt that it sells newspapers. The slick-paper picture magazines of large circulation have undoubtedly played an important role in dramatizing the mental changes that the psychedelic drugs bring about. I think it also fair to say that in doing so they have used a device that they commonly employ in treating of sex and violence in their pages: they deplore the excesses that they are at pains to picture, and they warn of dangers while at the same time suggesting the appeal of what they dramatize.

The biggest appeal that they suggest is freedom from the restraints of ordinary consciousness and everyday sorts of socialized behaviour. In one of the earliest picture stories on a psychedelic drug, in 1956, *Life* emphasized the use of *Psilocybe mexicana,* the so-called "sacred mushroom," in the service of religious visionary experience. Featured was the exotic ceremony of the Mazatec Indians of Mexico, who were pictured in their religious trances induced by the mushroom. Part of the dramatic contrast was furnished by the role played by Gordon Wasson, a presumably sensible New York banker, who with his wife and Roger Heim, the director of the Anthropological Museum in Paris, had organized the quest for the mushroom.

Life has run many stories since then on various psychedelic

* This paper is based in part on Chapter 21 of Mr. Barron's forthcoming book *Creativity and Personal Freedom,* which will be published in the fall of 1967 by D. Van Nostrand Company of Princeton, New Jersey.

drugs and on the entire psychedelic movement, devoting a special issue to the latter in 1965. *Look, Time, Holiday, Esquire, Saturday Evening Post* and *Playboy* have had one or more feature stories each since 1960. *Playboy,* as might be expected, was especially interested in the sex angle, and the recent *Playboy* interview with Timothy Leary featured the statement by Leary that "there is no question that LSD is the most powerful aphrodisiac ever discovered by man."

These articles not only sell magazines, they also sell LSD. The black-market operators in LSD have benefited from millions of dollars' worth of free advertising. I am not implying by this any *intent* on the part of popular magazines or newspapers, of course. Their job is to report the news, even if in reporting it they also help to create it.

It would be easy enough, as I have said, to base one's interpretation of the causes for the spread of the psychedelic drugs upon this arousal of popular interest through the mass communication media, especially if one adds to this the fact that the drugs do produce novel experiences and that mankind has always been willing to go to considerable lengths to break the monotony of life taken straight. And to these factors add the promise of the psychedelics that they bring the soul to God, or God to the soul, and perhaps even offer intimations of a personal life beyond the death of the body, and you have some historically proven motives for their use and a rational way of understanding their epidemic spread.

Yet these facts, though certainly relevant, are not, I believe, the whole story. To understand the psychedelic movement, we need to consider its historical context, *i.e.,* the historical moment itself in which the movement arises. We need also to get a more complete and factual picture of the psychological action of the psychedelic drugs and particularly to evaluate the claim that they result in an effective expansion of consciousness. Finally, perhaps, it would be fruitful to speculate upon the future, for perhaps the future is to some extent being shaped by the general movement of mind of which the psychedelic drugs are today the most newsworthy and vivid manifestation.

Let me begin by giving my own impression of "the historical moment."

The most striking thing about human culture in the twentieth century is the positive acceleration of the rate of change. This has become so generally evident since 1950 that the observation is by now a commonplace; however, the challenge that this presents to the psychological nature of man has perhaps not been fully recognized.

We should realize at the outset that at least some of the changes that are now occurring and others that are yet to come are a function simply of the increase of numbers of human beings, and this in turn involves the relationship of sexual reproduction to intelligence and culture. Samuel Butler's famous observation that a hen is an egg's way of producing another egg is relevant here. The germ-plasm may be understood as a stream that is relatively indifferent to the fate of its conduit. The hen is incapable of reflecting on this fact, but the human being may do so, and from this arises the unique status of *Homo sapiens* in biological evolution. This species alone has the power to affect the course of its own evolution by rational decision and, further, may even ask whether it is worth while to do so.

The increase in numbers, the so-called population explosion, is perhaps the most dramatic single index of the positive acceleration of the rate of change. The yearly worldwide increase at the present time is approximately 2%. Although seventy-five years were required for the world population to go from a half-billion to a billion (1850 to 1925), only thirty-seven years were required to go from one billion to two billion (1925 to 1962). Barring a general catastrophe or vastly increased control over reproduction, it will take only thirteen years (1962 to 1975) to go from two billion to three billion. And in seven years (1975 to 1982) the population of the world will reach four billion if the present rate of increase holds. A child born in 1962 will have seen the world's population double by the time he is twenty years old.

One of the odd and frequently overlooked facts about the population explosion is that it results in more brains. More brains think more thoughts, although, of course, they also think more of the *same* thoughts, and the most common thought is that which can be expected to show the greatest absolute increase in frequency. Nevertheless, as we know from psychological research with such devices as word-association tests, to name a convenient simple example, and from experiments contrasting the efficiency of groups with individuals in problem-solving, the greater the number of individuals who are thinking or responding, the greater also the absolute number of *singular* ideas and associations. With the vast increase in world population, it is reasonable to expect that the absolute number of highly original ideas will also show a large increase.

Very likely we are already witnessing this phenomenon and its results. Although other factors certainly enter in as well, it shows itself in the enormous increase in scientific and technological innovation. It has been estimated that 90% of all scientists who have ever lived are alive today. The amount of technical information doubles every ten years. The discovery of natural forces and the isolation of natural elements have been increasing at an exponential rate since 1850. During that same period of time there has been a vast increase in the availability of power to man through the control of energy sources. The steam engine, the gasoline-combustion engine, the electric generator and the nuclear reactor are step-by-step examples of this increase. There has also been a great increase in the range of perception of stimuli—more powerful microscopes and telescopes linked to photography, the discovery of radio followed by great advances in radio reception and transmission, the development of powerful audio-recorders and magnifiers, and the like. Add to these the vastly increased efficiency of electronic circuits through miniaturization and improved programming, the development of high-speed computers and automation and the enormous increase in speed and scope of communication as well as simple physical concentration of human beings in large and intricately organized ensembles, and the spectacle considered in the round is dizzying.

Is the psychological make-up of man adequate to the task of managing its own products? This is the question that the present generation has been called upon to face in the most urgent form in which it has ever been put. H. G. Wells in his last essay, "Mind at the End of its Tether," took a dismal view of the prospects, as indeed did such notable thinkers as William James, Sigmund Freud and C. S. Peirce as their own lives drew toward a close. Yet there is little point in listening to the pessimistic pronouncements of the old. It is for the young to take up the question; and if our youth today are singularly unwilling to heed their elders, and if they persist in seeking radically new ways of being and of experiencing, perhaps they are adopting a not wholly inappropriate strategy of search.

In seeking new ways of being and of experiencing, they start from rather stable reference points. In terms of intellectual ability of the sort commonly indicated by the term I.Q., which is to say "general intelligence," the present generation is certainly no different from its parents or grandparents. As various cross-sectional studies of school populations have shown, I.Q.'s in different parts of the world and in different parts of our own country, given reasonable similarity of environments, tend to have the same range, average value and variability. And this has probably been so for a long time. The distinguished paleontologist G. G. Simpson has estimated that the intelligence of *Homo sapiens* in this sense of the word intelligence has not changed for at least ten thousand years.

Let us grant, then, that general intelligence is quite stable in the individual and in the species. There is substantial evidence also that it is linked to genetic mechanisms of transmission, as studies of twin populations as well as parent-offspring correlations have shown. There is, of course, some possibility that advances in neurophysiology and biochemistry may change this situation, and eugenics remains a theoretical but politically remote possibility. But at the moment we must get used to the idea that if we are to solve our problems, we must be prepared to solve them with the same level of intelligence and the same biological nature that has brought us this far. One implication of this is that we must turn our attention more and more to the mechanisms for the transmission of culture, especially education. In the biological aspect of evolution we see organisms evolving; in the cultural aspect of evolution we see the generation and reproduction of new ideas, new social organizations, new ways of interpreting knowledge, new values and, to come to the point, new forms of consciousness. It is to this latter point that I now turn.

Rather than speaking of measured intelligence that is stable for the individual over time, because it is defined as the ratio of mental age to chronological age, we shall now speak of intelligence as *the content of what is intellected* and *the developing capacities for further intellection*. In this sense of the term, intelligence is continuously growing both for the individual and for the species. It is meaningful to say that we as individuals are more intelligent than we were a few years ago and that our children will be more intelligent than we are. Note also that in this sense of the term it is quite conceivable that small initial differences may result in vast terminal differences in "the intellected."

Something of the sort has indeed been happening in the development of the increasing superiority of man over other organisms and his increasing scope in comprehending himself and the world about him. Although we are on unsure speculative ground in attempting to identify the crucial stages in the evolution of consciousness, we may at any rate guess that as *Homo sapiens* gradually differentiated himself from the family of *Hominidae* by acquiring the ability not only to *use* tools but to *use tools to make tools,* an accompanying awareness of superior adaptability occurred. At some very early point there must have come, too, the kind of self-awareness that makes death an important subjective fact, an awareness that, coupled with primitive awe or bewilderment at the fact of being, serves as the basis of magic and religion. As animism grew more subtle in its personifications, mythic explanations of the origin of things became possible, and human-like gods were created. The passage to the idea of a single god, originated or at least dramatized by Akhnaton, led by linkage to the god of the Israelites and to the idea of Christ. Meanwhile the development of a conscious science (essentially, the evolution of canons of evidence for belief in the regularity of events in nature) had occurred, beginning with the Miletians in early Greece. Perhaps it is not too fanciful to suggest that the analogue to the achievement of early man in "making tools to make tools" is the scientific method: not just "knowing how to learn" but "knowing how to make sure that we know."

These twin achievements, separated by at least a hundred thousand years, are the fundaments of technology and science. They increased vastly the range of what might be intellected as well as the capacities for intellection. Scientific thought itself then produced several radical developments in man's self-awareness: the Copernican revolution, showing us something of the place of our earth in the universe; the Darwinian revolution, showing us something of our place in organic evolution; and what I shall call the Cartesian-Freudian revolution, for Freud completed what Descartes began, showing us the existence of vast reaches of mind beyond our conscious, rational mental processes. Hundreds of geniuses of the life of the psyche had, of course, known and expressed intuitively before Freud the mysteries of the unconscious; his achievement was simply the climax of an increasingly popular development in European thought. As L. L. Whyte in his book *The Unconscious before Freud* has shown quite convincingly, the idea of the unconscious was, as he says, *conceivable* around 1700, *topical* around 1800 and *effective* around 1900. By 1950 its exploration by individuals through psychoanalysis could be described as commonplace. What we are witnessing today is the easy accessibility and mass distribution of means for producing experience of the usually unexperienced aspects of mental functioning. At least part of the meaning of LSD today is this: that chemical technology has made available to millions the experience of transcendence of the individual ego, which a century ago was available only to the disciplined mystic.

But there are, of course, more varied phenomena than the feeling of ego-transcendence produced by the psychedelic drugs, and there are more motives than the religio-mystical motive lying behind the present widespread use of LSD. The claim that the drugs "expand consciousness" refers to changes in several dimensions of experience. I should like to take a look at this claim by first making an admittedly approximate classification or typology of psychedelic drug users and their motives. It is approximate in several senses, but primarily, I think, in that the "types" that I name are actually defined by "salient motivations," and as usual in human affairs the motives in practice are quite mixed. The classes that I see are as follow:

1. *Persons interested in the experience primarily for reasons of aesthetic appreciation or expression.* These may or may not be artists, but their attitude toward experience tends to be perceptually open and non-judgemental. These individuals especially seek and enjoy the perceptual changes, such as increased vividness of color, visual harmonies, change in depth perception, sharper definition of detail, synaesthesia, change in the time sense (especially when listening to music), increased volume of unusual imagery, and the like. The effects are, of course, not always beautiful and in fact

may be quite unpleasant; the "hellish" experience features garish or horrible colors (sickly greens, ugly dark reds, *etc.*) or sometimes an impression of threatening blackness accompanied by feelings of gloom and isolation. The person's perception of his own body may become unpleasant: his limbs may seem to be distorted or his flesh to be decaying; in a mirror his face may appear to be a mask, his smile a meaningless grimace; all human movements may seem mere puppetry, attempts at communication a mockery.

The claim that LSD is an aphrodisiac rests, of course, upon enhancement of sensual pleasure when the experience is a positive one. It should be made clear, however, that LSD is *not* an aphrodisiac, nor is it an anaphrodisiac, as indeed others have claimed. It intensifies whatever experience is occurring, pleasurable or unpleasurable. Two people in love with one another and genuinely close may experience an ecstasy of union; but if, alas, they are only pretending, they may experience a hell of isolation. If what is on the program is not love but simply sensual gratification—if the name of the game is sex—then intensified sexual experience may occur, although, again, quite the opposite may happen.

Even the negative aesthetic experience may not be seen by this group of people as truly negative, however; surrealism has in fact accustomed us to just such visions of the world. Among the aesthetic adepts there is even a phrase for the negative experience when it occurs: it is known as "paying your taxes." The so-called "bad trip" can also be interpreted in quite positive terms; it "tells you where you are," and if where you are is in confusion, pain or hypocrisy and sin, then you must be paying the price all the time anyhow. Better to face it now and suffer through.

2. *Persons interested primarily in religious experience,* whether in their own search for transcendent meaning or out of an interest in the psychology of religion or its philosophical bases. LSD may produce a feeling of oneness with the universe and a reduction or complete loss of the sense of personal identity. When this occurs, there seems no distinction between subject and object, all is seen as part of a cosmic process. An inner emptiness or silence, pertaining either to the interior of the self or to an "interior" of the universe, may be experienced and may come as an apparent revelation of divinity. Either the *fascinosum* or *tremen-*

dum, to use Rudolph Otto's terms, may be felt. The *fascinosum* is a feeling of joy, gratitude, pleasure or onrush of grace at catching a glimpse of the Ultimate or *numen;* the *tremendum* is a reaction of awe, horror, fear or a feeling of being overwhelmed. As in the aesthetic experience, both the negative and the positive are seen as valid and therefore endurable, or even welcome.

Included in this group of users of psychedelic substances is a wide range of people, from shamans of primitive tribes through the "mushroom magicians" of the Aztecs to contemporary theologians and students of comparative religion. The largest organized church founded on psychedelics is the Native American Church, which grew out of the peyotism of the Mescalero Apaches and spread to the Comanches, Kiowas and other Plains tribes. Havelock Ellis is an interesting example of a sophisticated European who sampled the peyote buttons in the service of his religious quest. He took them between noon and three o'clock on Good Friday, thus making fairly sure that his mind would be turned in the right direction for a Christian experience through the next several hours.

In my own view, let me add, an archetypal experience of Christ, *i.e.,* of Christ free from the institutional embodiment known as Christianity, is common to many psychedelic "trips." Christ on the cross may then be understood simply as consciousness impaled on the human form, mind hung to die on body to expiate our voluntary participation in the world's heavy materialism. This is, of course, not the historical Christ, but Christ as archetype and heart of myth; in historical persons myth becomes biography.

3. *Persons seeking a cure for alcoholism.* This group overlaps somewhat with the preceding group, even though the primary motive of its members is to obtain a cure of their addiction. It is interesting that the peyote cult began with somewhat the same motives. The "peyote boys," as they were known by other Indians, foreswore alcohol as one of the conditions of membership. William James once observed that "the best cure for dipsomania is religiomania," and peyotism in a sense is an Indian cure for a white man's disease. Recent research on the effects of alcohol on fantasy show that the release of inhibitions on sexual and aggressive impulses is no greater a motive for drinking than is the desire for what the investigators call "meaning contrasts," which on closer examina-

tion prove to be very similar to philosophizing about the meaning of life. Experience in the treatment of alcoholism with LSD shows that occurrence of "the transcendental experience" is the most important ingredient in the cure.

4. *Persons seeking relief from personal psychological problems of a neurotic sort.* LSD is used by this group under psychiatric or psychological supervision, primarily for catharsis, for the uncovering of repressed memories and affects and for confrontation with the "real self." Combined with therapeutic interviews before and after the LSD experience, treatment has proved just as effective as conventional psychotherapy over a much longer period of time. The data published by Robert E. Mogar and Charles Savage [Personality change associated with psychedelic (LSD) therapy: a preliminary report. *Psychotherapy,* Fall, 1964] reveal that patients in LSD therapy improve significantly in ego-strength and show a marked reduction in depression and hypochondriasis. *ı*

5. *Seriously disturbed persons who are potentially suicidal or psychotic* and who use the drugs on their own and out of a sense of desperation. A characteristic expression of persons in this group is that they want to "break through." To such persons LSD seems their last chance; and when it fails to produce the "breakthrough," it may leave them feeling hopeless and in an even more chaotic psychic state than before. A certain number of such persons have in essence already quit life and are simply looking for something to carry them over the edge to oblivion. These are the rare cases, of course, but they do provide the headlines when they come to grief. Generally they would have come to psychiatric attention in any event. Such "cases" would never be given LSD by a psychiatrist or psychologist, but instead they would be provided with close therapeutic support of a realistic sort, possibly in a hospital. They are people who have been badly hurt by life and who need the help of physicians and nurses to get back on their own feet again.

6. *Persons who are chronic social delinquents* and who turn to all sorts of drugs in an effort to escape themselves. These are the so-called "sociopaths," who occur in some number in every generation, the flotsam and jetsom of society, who in childhood never acquired the bases of moral distinction or of social responsibility.

Among them are those who hate their homes and hate their native land, perhaps because their own childhood need to love was defeated. I have no idea what the frequency of use may be in this group, but my impression is that they tend not to like the psychedelic drug experience and not to repeat it, unless its use serves their more basic motive of hatred of the social order that stands in place of the defeating family.

When used by persons in these two latter classes of users, the psychiatrically disturbed and the socially delinquent, LSD and other psychedelic drugs do indeed seem to be "dangerous." It should be noted, however, that there is no evidence that LSD is "dangerous" in the sense that thalidomide is dangerous, or heroin, or methyl alcohol, or tobacco. These substances are known to pose a threat to the human organism in that they attack its physical or physiological substrate and may bring about enduring physical or physiological changes. If LSD does this, no evidence has yet been brought forward to establish the fact.

Nonetheless, LSD *is* unquestionably very dangerous in some persons, namely in dangerous persons, *i.e.,* persons who are dangerous to themselves or to others. These generally are persons whom society has served ill. If they are numerous, perhaps it is because society itself is dangerous. The baby born into this world faces innumerable hazards, and society protects it from a multitude of those hazards, but at the expense of exposing the new human being to a process requiring renunciations of impulse and feelings that may burden it with great psychic distress and permanent and pervasive unhappiness. These unhappy persons, who have been born into life willy-nilly and inducted into society willy-nilly, may choose as they grow older to leave the one or to reject the other. Insofar as they use a drug such as LSD to abet their purposes, it may be said to be, like firearms, something that society in its wisdom should control. Society has not, it must be admitted, controlled firearms, neither the little guns nor the big ones. Our own country attempted to prohibit alcohol and failed. Perhaps the proper course is to define the sorts of behavior with these potentially dangerous things that can be considered acceptable and not dangerous and then to impose legal sanctions against behavior that does in fact cause harm or disturb the public order. Application of such criteria would certainly help to clarify the situation today with respect to the widespread use of marijuana, and perhaps it is applicable as well to the use of the more powerful drugs such as LSD.

7. *Persons in late adolescence or early adulthood whose psychological development has encountered the "identity crisis" and who are in the process of sorting out from among various possible identities the ones that fit best their interests, values and capabilities.* Most commonly these are college students who are basically quite healthy psychologically and who are experiencing the classical *"Sturm und Drang"* of late adolescence. They are trying to "make up their minds" among many possible choices, often with a dim awareness that there are elections or options that cannot be articulated at present. Essentially they are asking the question "What can I be *now* that will enable me to be a worthwhile and self-esteemed person ten or twenty years from now?" Many of them feel that their education is lagging in preparing them for what they will be called upon to be in the future. These students, while remaining tentative, turn to LSD in the hope that it will tell them something about themselves and will help to clarify the possibilities for future development. They are probably the largest single group of users of LSD. Their source of supply at present is necessarily the black-market. A major problem arising from the new laws is that civil authority thus becomes alienated from young people, who have great potential for contributing to the society of the future. In a healthy society, the intellectually able and creative citizens serve to vivify and to support the social authority; but if they are defined as enemies of society for pursuing activities that they consider constructive, they will incorporate into their personal identity significant elements of anti-sociality.

Indeed, there is already developing a sort of "LSD underground man," in the Dostoevskian sense of the term—a man who, in Dostoevski's words, "would rather that his hand wither off than that he carry a single brick to help build the crystal palace," the crystal palace being the world that modern science and technology and state collectivism are making. These individuals, both students and non-students, use LSD in the service of an apocalyptic vision of the future of mankind. That vision takes many forms, but a common element is the development of radically new relationships between the individual and the state, including the development of new social institutions to replace marriage and family. These young people feel very keenly the invasion of privacy by the police and by state "information-collectors." They seek a human nature that will be free of the tyranny of the machine. Their shibboleth is "the acid test;" the civil rights movement is involved too, for "color dissolves in acid." The "acid test" is at least in part the ability to abandon the claims of the individual ego and to participate in a sort of group mind that is preparing to "take off" and is just about ready to "go somewhere." The analogy of the psychedelic trip to the space journey seems to have begun about 1955, and, we can suppose, entered the imagination through the news.

Another recurring theme in this group is that "history is ending," or sometimes, less cosmically, that "Christianity is ending." Some indeed say that the world is about to end and that the expansion of consciousness is isomorphic with the expansion of the physical universe, that both will fall back to the center simultaneously and instantaneously and all vanish in a trice. Still others see the world as ending in a nuclear explosion. Whatever the vision, the world as we know it now, *i.e.,* modern society, is seen as fleeting, perishable, not viable.

And it does no good to ask what rearrangement of things as they are is being proposed by these youth. Nothing is being proposed, and they see it as the nature of the case that nothing *can* be proposed. You can ask a person to imagine pink elephants or rhinoceroses with horses' heads or skyscrapers that walk and talk, but you cannot ask him to imagine an unknown primary color. There is a new time coming, and we shall know what it is when it happens. LSD, as interpreted by this group, is the source of the energy that is to transform human intelligence and consciousness.

The motive for this sort of exploration of the potentialities of the mind is an extraordinarily powerful one. It is in essence highly idealistic and moral, regardless of its association with behavior that much of society may consider immoral. Indeed, it may even arise in part because of the basic human need to feel worth while through knowing that one is behaving responsibly and in a way that makes sense to others. If the population explosion does in fact demand that the satisfaction of sexual needs be sundered from its immemorial partner, sexual reproduction, then a new morality must be created. The members of this LSD in-group understand one another and buttress one another's sense of self-esteem. To them LSD does not seem dangerous to those who use it, but to those who do not use it, for those who do not use it will be left behind as human nature enters the new millennium.

Whether or not LSD as used by these various groups serves to "expand consciousness" is the question that I should now like to consider. The meaning that I give to this term requires that consciousness remain expanded or extended after the primary drug effects have worn off. On the premise that consciousness, like intelligence, is not unitary, I have attempted on introspective grounds to identify several dimensions or factors. The ones that I suggest as main dimensions, with apologies for their murkiness, are as follows.

1. *The range of effective attention.* People certainly differ in their responsiveness to the wide variety of signals or cues, inner and outer, potentially available to them. We gauge a man's scope in part by the range of his attention, not only over the objects in his present ken, but over all that has ever occurred to him. One of the most ancient and persistent of religious ideas is that through constant and honest attention to all the acts of one's life one can escape the cycle of birth and death. The Buddha at his death is said to have had present in his consciousness the totality not only of his final incarnation but of all the incarnations through which he had passed. Henry James's famous injunction "Be a person on whom nothing is lost" expresses the value of sensitive and unforgetting attention. The great act of attention is all-inclusive; the more of life that is remembered and brought to bear upon the present moment in living expression, the more fully *conscious* a person may be said to be.

2. *Realization of depths or heights of the self for which no words exist.* As you might expect, this dimension is rather difficult to define. I can only appeal from my introspection to your introspection in offering it for consideration. What I mean here is something akin to Plato's idea of the "musical unconscious," or as he also called it, "the spiritual unconscious." Rainer Maria Rilke has perhaps come closest to expressing it both in *The Duino Elegies* and in his *Sonnets to Orpheus*. In the concluding sonnet of the

Orpheus cycle occur these three lines, which may serve to evoke my meaning:

> *Be* the magic power of this immense
> midnight at the crossroads of your senses
> *be* the purport of their strange meeting.

3. *Sensitivity to the breadth of consciousness of others, including animals.* This would involve also a recognition of the "game" character of social interaction and personal relationship—at a low level, an awareness of "the games people play," including oneself of course; and at a high level an appreciation of mythic enactment in human affairs, the extent to which the roles that are possible to us because of our evolutionary history find expression in any given time-stretch in our lives. Ovid's *Metamorphoses* provides an excellent inventory of such possibilities.

4. *Ability to observe, yet not to observe, the subject-object distinction, as well as other perceptual constancies and conceptual-perceptual habits.* Essentially this involves a freedom from the constraints of learned adaptive mechanisms, which implies that they can be used in a highly disciplined manner whenever appropriate. Many of the saints in the various world religions provide us with examples of this capacity, for the saint is very often a hard worker who is expert in the ways of the world, a "practical transcendentalist" who "has the best of both worlds."

We may now ask whether LSD results in an extension of any of these abilities. There is no answer available in current psychological research. The occurrence of the *appearance* of such phenomena in written or recorded accounts of drug sessions is not really evidence. I would not be willing to say that consciousness has been expanded or extended unless it could be shown to be so when the person is in his normal state, free of drug effects. In brief, my view is that the intact ego, in which all the capacities of mind are used to the fullest, is the best vehicle that we have for bringing ourselves into valid and discriminating relationship with the protean forms of reality. The evolutionary task, both in the individual and in the species, is to create an ego that is itself capable of including the states of consciousness that we now call paranormal. The states that the psychedelic drugs produce should not themselves be confused with "expanded consciousness." That comes later, if it comes at all, when and if the experience of unusual realities is brought into the ego and the ego itself is thereby enlarged in scope.

A corollary of this is that the ego already possessed of considerable scope is more likely to be able to use such an experience to grow further and to enlarge itself, just as it is the stronger ego that can use psychotherapy more effectively.

Finally, however, it should be said that in some unknown but probably considerable percentage of cases the psychedelic drugs do lead the individual towards further exploration of consciousness *without* further use of the drugs. This I think is the desideratum. William James has given us a compelling account of this stimulus to further work by his own experience of nitrous-oxide intoxication. Consider this quotation from *The Varieties of Religious Experience:*

> One conclusion was forced upon my mind at that time, and my impression of its truth has ever since remained unshaken. It is that our normal waking consciousness, rational consciousness as we call it, is but one special type of consciousness, whilst all about it, parted from it by the filmiest of screens, there lie potential forms of consciousness entirely different. We may go through life without suspecting their existence; but apply the requisite stimulus, and at a touch they are there in all their completeness, definite types of mentality which probably somewhere have their field of application. No account of the universe in its totality can be final which leaves these other forms of consciousness disregarded. How to regard them is the question—for they are so discontinuous with ordinary consciousness. Yet they may determine attitudes though they cannot furnish formulas, and open a region though they fail to give a map. At any rate, they forbid a premature closing of our accounts with reality.

The phrase "determine attitudes" seems especially important to me in this passage from William James. Individuals who have presentiments of a future for human consciousness, or perhaps simply for consciousness, human or not, that includes transcendence of material form have an especial attitude toward the phenomena produced by the psychedelic drugs. The attitude is more than one of openness; it is better described as one of expectancy; at any rate, judgement from the established viewpoint of materialistic science is held in abeyance. This expectation, let me add, is very different from the hope for personal survival of bodily death or for novelty of experience in the individual life. Of all the motives for courting the psychedelic experience, this is the most personally disinterested and, of course, the most esoteric.

Closer to commonsense, though still perhaps rather "far out," is the view that human consciousness is in the process of pushing beyond the limits of the Freudian unconscious. Control of nuclear energy, the most extraordinary practical result of the Einsteinian revolution in cosmology, has brought man face to face with his own limits, and he must recognize the possibility that the uninterrupted development of human intelligence applied to science may bring self-destruction. The extension of human consciousness thus offers a hope that new forms of community may be found in which conceptual, science-making intelligence and aggressive, territorial instincts will be less necessary and can be reduced or transcended.

When such an intuition or reasoned expectation motivates persons of power in the "real" world, such as political, economic and religious leaders (perhaps even including the owners of newspaper, magazine and television syndicates), the possibility of a general change in human consciousness as a result of widely shared new experiences of the reaches of consciousness is greatly enhanced. I feel that something of this sort is what is happening now.

2   The Therapeutic Potential of LSD in Medicine*

By ALBERT A. KURLAND *with* CHARLES SAVAGE, JOHN W. SHAFFER *and* SANFORD UNGER

INTRODUCTION

HISTORICALLY the use of LSD-type drugs in psychiatric treatment is as ancient as the written records of man. Three millennia ago the East already had its legendary soma, and the West its nepenthe. Possibly more ancient even than these is the use of the hemp derivative marijuana, mentioned in 2737 B.C. in the writings of the Chinese emperor Shen Neng. The search for and preoccupation with substances that might help man to transcend himself permeate almost every civilization known to mankind. One can cross a bridge of centuries to the Indian cultures of Central America. Here the explorers of the American continents found the Aztec priests using certain plants to bring about communion with their gods and to induce visions. In addition, the plants were widely employed among the populace for purposes of sorcery and healing. Much of our knowledge of this facet of civilization's course, along with an account of the controversy centering around the use of these substances, is summarized in the recent book by Masters and Houston, *The Varieties of Psychedelic Experience* (Masters and Houston, 1966).

LSD was first synthesized at the Sandoz Research Laboratories in Basle, Switzerland, in 1938, by Stoll and Hofmann. It was not until 1943, however, that Hofmann accidentally discovered the hallucinogenic properties of the drug. Initially, the unique effects and the extreme potency of the compound suggested its possibilities as an agent for producing a temporary "model psychosis."

Following publication of the first reports on LSD, research began by focussing on its psychotomimetic properties. However, the opportunity to produce a controllable state that activated emo-

* This study was made possible by United States Public Health Service Grants *MH 08474* and *MH 11001* from the National Institutes of Health and through the assistance of Friends of Psychiatric Research, Inc.

tions ranging from anxiety to euphoria and that increased association and recall, accompanied by episodes of catharsis and abreaction, suggested possibilities for therapeutic use for rapidly gaining access to chronically withdrawn patients. In one of the earliest studies, entitled "Lysergic Acid Diethylamide (LSD-25) as an Aid in Psychotherapy," Busch and Johnson observed that patients were able to verbalize the repressed components of their conflicts during LSD intoxication (Busch and Johnson, 1950).

In 1952 Savage reported the first study attempting to use LSD, in very minute doses, as a chemotherapeutic drug, namely as a euphoriant in the treatment of depressions. Savage concluded that no significant therapeutic advantage seemed to be achieved (Savage, 1952).

By 1954, Sandison and his co-workers reported a continuing series of investigations of LSD as an aid to psychotherapy. Their conclusion was that LSD "produces an upsurge of unconscious material into consciousness" and that "repressed memories are relived with remarkable clarity—with therapeutically beneficial consequences" (Sandison, Spencer and Whitelaw, 1954; Sandison, 1954; Sandison and Whitelaw, 1957).

From these early investigations, followed by the work of Abramson (Abramson, 1955, 1960), of Ling and Buckman (Ling and Buckman, 1960) and especially of Leuner and Holfeld (Leuner and Holfeld, 1964), there was developed the technique conceptualized as psycholytic psychotherapy. In this technique, which is psychoanalytically oriented, the therapist employs the drug on a repeated basis, at a low dosage, usually of 50 μg to 70 μg, during the course and within the framework of continuing psychotherapy. The administration of the drug is conceived to facilitate recall, reliving, catharsis and abreaction, with the production of associational, dreamlike material for subsequent analysis.

In 1957 Osmond (Osmond, 1957) introduced a different technique, utilizing a single high dose of LSD. "Our work started," he stated, "with the idea that a single overwhelming experience might be beneficial to alcoholics, the idea springing from James (James, 1906) and Tiebout (Tiebout, 1954)." There was now an increasing interest in the use of environmental stimuli, such as music, to guide and program the course of the reaction, probably deriving from a familiarity with the techniques employed by the Indians of the Native American Church in their use of peyote.

The further development of this concept and associated techniques is now called psychedelic therapy. It is a highly specialized form of brief intensive psychotherapy. Its emergence as a distinctive treatment form is based on the reliable reproducibility of the psychedelic reaction, which in non-drug contexts has been referred to as a "peak," "identity" or "conversion" experience. Such episodes produced with the aid of LSD in dosages of 200 μg or more are characterized subjectively by a profound depth and intensity of positive emotion.

In general theoretical terms, pathological functioning in the patient is presumed to have been determined by a reinforcement history that would have predisposed toward root "defects" in the self-system (self-image, self-esteem, self-trust, sense of basic worth) and associated value-attitude distortions and "inadequacies." The major effort of psychedelic therapy is reconstructive, premised on the possibility—via the psychedelic reaction—of rapidly establishing and then consolidating the patient's functioning on a core of positive self-acceptance and regard. The technique requires an especially trained therapist, who, assisted by a nurse, is in constant attendance during the entire period of the ten to twelve hours of the LSD session. The therapist is responsible for guiding, shaping and programming the course of the session, remaining flexibly attuned to the patient's progress, giving reassurance, aborting anxiety or other turbulent disturbing emotional states or disruptive episodes, mobilizing and integrating affective responses and dynamic material as the patient's experiences unfold, *etc*. It should be emphasized that the LSD session follows intensive therapeutic preparation for a period of two to four weeks. After the LSD session therapy is required to work through, support and redirect the patient. If clinical judgment indicates, the patient may have further treatment with LSD.

CLINICAL STUDIES

In the studies carried out to date (March, 1967) at Spring Grove State Hospital in Baltimore, Maryland, over 177 patients, predominantly neurotic and alcoholic, have been treated. In the controlled phase of this work, now under way, patients are systematically followed at six, twelve and eighteen months, and their courses evaluated by an independent assessment team. Although the studies are not complete, there are strong preliminary indications that the psychedelic procedure does significantly facilitate therapy.

Some case-history material may illustrate this treatment process in more detail as well as some of its unusual advantages.

Patient A–1, a forty-year-old Negro, was brought to the hospital from jail after drinking uncontrollably for ten days. He had been draining whiskey barrels at his place of work, a distillery. He gave a history of excessive alcohol consumption during the past four years. He had a continual flow of drinking associates in the taverns and homes and on the sidewalks of his neighborhood. The only limit on his drinking was his low income and the need to support five children. During these years his marriage had deteriorated. He had grown up on a tenant farm and dropped out of the fourth grade at the age of twelve. He was an unskilled laborer. On mental status he appeared as intellectually dull. He seemed to be passive and submissive and able to feel like a man only when he had a bottle in his hand. On psychological testing he achieved a full-scale Wechsler I.Q. of 70. He scored in the 88th percentile on the Eysenck Neuroticism Scale. The Minnesota Multiphasic Personality Inventory (MMPI) indicated severe depression, anxiety and a schizoid pattern of adjustment.

During his LSD session, he felt he was being chased, stricken with a sword, run over by a horse and frightened by a hippopotamus. In his written report, he stated:

> I was afraid. I started to run, but something said 'Stop!' When I stopped, everything broke into many pieces. Then I felt as if ten tons had fallen from my shoulders. I prayed to the Lord. Everything looked better all around me. The rose was beautiful. My children's faces cleared up. I thought of alcohol and the rose died. I changed my mind from alcohol toward Christ and the rose came back to life. I pray that this rose will remain in my heart and my family forever. As I sat up and looked in the mirror, I could feel myself growing stronger. I feel now that my family and I are closer than ever before, and I hope that our faith will grow forever and ever.

This particular patient was fortunate in having a family that reinforced his new-found feeling of love and affection for them. A patient who goes back to a rejecting family is very likely to return to drink.

One week after LSD therapy the patient was retested. His score on the neuroticism scale had fallen to the 10th percentile. His I.Q., however, had remained constant, although with some patients we see a rather startling rise in the I.Q. as tested. The MMPI depression score was markedly improved. At the sixth-month interview the MMPI was within normal limits. He had been totally abstinent, and his wife reported that there was a peace and harmony in the home that had never existed before and that he had never been better. At twelve months the family picture remains the same. He is still sober, although there has been one brief break in abstinence following the loss of his job. What seems striking about this particular case is not only that an alcoholic's drinking has been arrested, but that an illiterate, culturally deprived man of low intelligence could apparently be reached through a psychotherapeutic procedure. This is in stark contrast to the general notion that lower-class patients are not amenable to psychotherapeutic intervention.

Patient N–2, a twenty-three-year-old white female, had one illegitimate child. She had four admissions to Spring Grove starting at the age of fifteen. On the first admission she was hospitalized for eighteen months; on the second admission, for twelve months. The patient was admitted to the hospital on each occasion because of severe depressive reactions. The background data indicate a great deal of sociopathic behavior, a rather promiscuous sexual history and general instability. During one of her hospitalizations, she had received prolonged psychotherapy. Subsequently she was also treated with a variety of psychotropic drugs (antidepressants, antianxiety agents and antipsychotic medication) without any particularly significant results. The patient's Raven I.Q. was tested at 94. Clinical evaluation of the pre-treatment MMPI is reproduced below:

> The profile of this patient suggests the presence of severe psychopathology. Primary elevations are on scales measuring psychopathy and unusualness of thought content. Secondary elevations are on scales measuring depression and anxiety—

'psychic pain,' in short. Diagnostically, this is the profile of a personality disorder, currently experiencing severe anxiety and depression. Reality contact appears tenuous, and psychotic episodes are a distinct possibility. Poor judgment and impulsive acting-out are likely characteristics. The relatively low *Mf* score in the presence of the other scale elevations suggests masochistic feminine attitudes.

After several weeks of preliminary psychotherapy, the LSD session was undertaken. This young woman wrote an articulate account of her LSD experience, and since it further illustrates both details of the technique and the dramatic impact that the LSD session may achieve, the complete report is reproduced here.

The LSD-Session Report of Patient N–2

I must admit that in the beginning, I was quite apprehensive and more than a little afraid. The nurse had come and got me at about eight-thirty. I felt a little more comfortable when I got in the treatment room where I had spent so many hours in therapy. When the doctor came in, I was even more comforted as I knew he understood and would be there to help and guide me.

I drank my LSD at 8:45. From that point on time had no perspective. The doctor, the nurse, and I looked at some pictures of myself and my family. I began to feel dizzy and wanted to lie down. Then I thought I'd better go to the bathroom first. When I got up, the floor seemed to tilt and roll. It wasn't an unpleasant sensation, however. I came back from the bathroom and the eyeshades and earphones were put into place. The doctor squeezed my hand and suddenly I wasn't afraid anymore. I drifted with the music and was at one with the music.

My sense of touch became very intensified. The blanket that was covering me became alive. I remember touching my face and feeling every particle of my skin.

I was drifting with the music and I had the sense that I was dying. I was at my funeral. I could smell all of the flowers. I cried, but I didn't want to escape from the feeling. I somehow knew that I had to die in order to be born again.

The music was stopped and the eyeshades and earphones

removed. The colors in the room were vibrating and alive. I talked with the doctor and asked him if I had died. I was still crying.

I lay back down and the shades and earphones were put in place. Again, I drifted with the music.

Suddenly my body seemed to grow very warm. I felt with every sense of my being that I was in hell. My body grew warmer and warmer, then suddenly burst into fire. I was afraid; then the doctor took my hand. I lay there and let my body burn up. The fire seemed to cleanse me. Then all sensation seemed to fade and I asked to sit up.

The doctor showed me some pictures. One was called The Guardian Angel. To me, at the time, it represented a mother and child. I said with amazement, 'It's me. I'm crying. My baby!'

All at once, after all the doubts and fears, I knew I was a mother and that I loved my child.

The earphones and shades were put back in place and the music playing was 'The Lord's Prayer.' There must have been a short pause in the music but to me it seemed an eternity. I said, 'Don't stop it. God is whole in me!' At this point, I felt as if God were holding me in His arms and revealing Himself to me. I smiled and said, 'I've found Him, I've found Him.' I had such a tremendous sense of peace and well being. After so many years of running alone and afraid, God was now with me.

The music stopped and I lay relaxed and said, 'But I found a reason for it all.' God's place in the universe, in the world, and in myself seemed so clear. He is love and He is life. He is in everything. And finally, at long last, He was also in me.

I looked at a picture of my son and I felt an overwhelming sense of love and for the first time gratitude for my motherhood. I was crying but crying with joy and thankfulness. I wiped away the cleansing, wonderful tears.

I then looked at a picture of myself when I was fifteen. I knew that the girl in the picture never was; the person was never real. I tore up the picture and pointed to myself. 'This is what she is.' I was on the road to discovering myself.

It was now 11:20. I had been under the LSD for only three

hours; however, it seemed as if it had been eternities. I had no sense of time. I can remember at one point asking the doctor what time it was and he answered, 'Twenty minutes to eternity.'

I lay relaxed and smoked a cigarette. I was shown a picture of the Christ Child and His mother. I said with wonder, 'She's not afraid of Him— I'm not afraid!' It had been fear of love that had kept me from loving my son.

The earphones and shades were put in place and again I drifted with the music. I had a tremendous sense of life and living. I exclaimed, 'I'm alive!' I had only existed. The music again paused and again I said, 'Don't let it go away. I don't want it to go away!'

Then the music changed. The record was Mahalia Jackson. The sound pounded around me. It seemed as if the music was trying to consume me. I knew fear, stark, naked fear. Fear was all around me, covering me. The music shouted at me and vibrated through me. I tore off the earphones and shades and shouted, 'Turn it off.' It was as if it didn't stop, it would destroy me.

The doctor turned off the music and blessed silence filled the room. I said, 'I don't think I've ever been so afraid.' I knew then that I was running away. My words were, 'I was running away, wasn't I? I was all the way back to hell and I wasn't afraid. What frightened me? I was never so afraid!'

The doctor talked to me of fear and fear of fear. I realized that I had been consumed with fear all my life. He said, 'This is the time. Let's go toward it.' I said, 'I'm afraid—I don't want to go.'

Then suddenly I knew that I had to face whatever there was to come. It was now or never. I held to the doctor's hand and said, 'Don't let me run anymore.' I was too tired to run anymore.

The music again took over and I felt comforted. I relaxed and was just one with the music.

When the music stopped. I looked about the room and the colors were alive. They glowed. I wanted a purple glass that was on the table. I wanted to feel the color. I seemed to be one with the soft glowing purple.

I went to the bathroom and looked out the window. The

earth seemed to vibrate with life. I exclaimed, 'It's alive. It's a wonderful world. I don't have to run anymore.'

Back in the treatment room the rose seemed to radiate life. I felt it, smelled it, savored it.

Again the shades and earphones were put into place and I drifted with the music. The record was 'Oh Come Immanuel.' Again, I had the sense of being with God. He was holding me in His arms and He was revealing life to me. Then suddenly, light was all around me, and love, wonderful, overwhelming love, was all around me.

I could love and be loved. After so many years of wandering I had come home. My words were, 'I have so much to give. I've been so empty—that's not important now.' I was crying for joy and thankfulness. I had received the most priceless gifts there are—the gifts of life and love. The music continued and I cried, 'I'm crying for joy!'

The music stopped and I removed the shades and earphones and sat up. The doctor gave me a mirror. I looked and saw myself. I radiated love. I said, 'I see love, so much love. I was there all along. Oh, I love me.'

I know now where I was. I was at the beginning of my life. I had just been born. I was alive! After twenty-three dead, wasted years, I had been born. Thank God I was finally alive! I said in awe, 'I don't have to run anymore. I can be with myself—it's so wonderful, so wonderful. I'm so thankful. I can just feel it all over me.'

Again, I went back with the music and knew only joy. The music flowed over me and I was elated. The sound flowed through every fiber of my body. The music stopped and I laughed and laughed with pure joy. I asked for a drink of water and it was nectar. I cried, 'I want to embrace the whole world.' I found God—it was so important. I'm not alone any more. I'll never be alone again! I looked at a picture of my son, and felt as if I would burst with love.

Again I listened to the music. When it stopped, I looked at a picture of my mother. The hate I had once felt dissolved and I knew only compassion. I said, 'I feel sorry for her.'

I went again to the bathroom and this time the sun came in

through the window and I travelled up the rays and went into the sun. I was warm and dancing and vibrating with golden color.

Once again I returned to the couch and listened to the music. When the music stopped, the doctor and I had sandwiches. I ate a salami sandwich and relished every bite. I can truthfully say it was the best thing I've ever eaten.

Later the doctor and I went for a walk and I literally discovered the world. I saw, smelled, and touched the trees, flowers, and grass. I touched the bark of a tree and felt the life running through it feeding the deep green leaves. I touched the grass and it felt like velvet. The soft warm air embraced me. This was life; this way my world and I was at home.

We returned to the treatment room and continued to listen to music. The music seemed to reach and awaken a depth in me that I never knew existed. When Beethoven's ninth was playing, I was completely at one with the music. With each note I seemed to soar to higher heights.

At about 9:00 I returned to the ward and drifted off into a dreamless sleep. When I awoke, the next morning, I saw my rose on the nightstand and for the first time in my life, I thanked God that I was alive.

Patient N–2's post-session Raven I.Q. tested at 112, a significant increase over the pre-treatment score of 94. Her MMPI, administered one week after the session, reports the following:

> Post LSD-session, marked improvement has taken place in a number of symptom areas. Depression and anxiety have both been reduced to within normal limits. Perhaps even more striking, however, has been the reduction in psychotic elements. Reality contact appears firm and there is no longer any suggestion of an imminent psychotic break. However, although the patient is undoubtedly more psychologically comfortable, in view of the continuing indications of an 'acting out' personality disorder, any long-range prognosis must be guarded.

After LSD the therapeutic task remains of effectively reinforcing the patient's committment to his discovered potentials, of consolidating a set of stable "self-equilibrating" reactions, which will call the patient back to his "new identity" whenever relapses into old thought and feeling patterns occur.

Therapy continued with patient N–2 for six months, largely on an out-patient basis but including rehospitalization for one additional LSD session. The last follow-up interview with the patient, conducted fifteen months after her initial entry into therapy, reported on her course and status as follows:

> After her second LSD session, the patient went to work as an aide at a private mental hospital where she lived in. While there, she met and befriended a young male patient of very good family background. A satisfying relationship developed and was continued after the patient's discharge.
>
> During this time, patient N–2 consented to the adoption of her son. She states that she worked out her guilt over this matter and feels sure that it was in the best interest of the child.
>
> Shortly thereafter, in a church wedding, and with the consent and approval of the groom's parents as well as her own, she was married to the aforesaid ex-patient. From that time to date, she has had a more satisfying and meaningful adjustment than ever in her life.
>
> At times there have been rough spots in her relationship with her husband who is finding his own way since his hospitalization. However, there have been no unsurmountable problems and this period has been stable. She seems to feel more sure of herself and more comfortable than this interviewer has ever seen her before.

Treatment of *Patient D–1* involved our most recent and intriguing area of investigation. It concerns the use of psychedelic therapy with terminal-cancer patients in an effort to alleviate psychological distress and deepen philosophical perspective. Kast has reported favorably on the use of LSD with patients in this category (Kast, 1964).

Our initial exploration of the relevance of this treatment form for patients with terminal diagnoses was quite unplanned. A professional member of our own research department, a woman in her early forties, developed a progressive neoplastic disease. She had undergone radical mastectomy, and subsequent surgery had revealed inoperable metastases to the liver. Although still ambulatory, she was in considerable physical distress—unable even to breathe deeply without severe pain. She was fully aware of the gravity of her condition, and her depressed and distraught psychological state was steadily worsening.

Our colleague, while not herself directly associated with the LSD projects, was conversant with the nature of the work. She requested treatment. After discussion with her husband and her surgeon and with the approval of all concerned, a course of psychedelic therapy was initiated.

Preparation for the LSD session occupied somewhat over a week. It focussed on the issue of personal identity and the state of important current relationships. Two days after the 200-μg session Patient D–1 went on vacation with her husband and children. Upon return, two weeks after the session, she completed the report which is reproduced below.

The LSD-Session Report of Patient D–1

The day prior to LSD, I was fearful and anxious. I would, at that point, have gratefully withdrawn. By the end of the preparatory session, practically all anxiety was gone, the instructions were understood, the procedure clear. The night was spent quietly at home; close friends visited, and we looked at photograph albums and remembered happy family times. Sleep was deep and peaceful. I awakened refreshed, and with practically no fear. I felt ready and eager.

The morning was lovely—cool and with a freshness in the air. I arrived at the LSD building with the therapist. Members of the department were around to wish me well. It was a good and warming feeling.

In the treatment room was a beautiful happiness rosebud, deep red and dewey, but disappointingly not as fragrant as other varieties. A bowl of fruit, moist, succulent, also reposed on the table. I was immediately given the first dose and sat looking at pictures from my family album. Gradually my movements became fuzzy and I felt awkward. I was made to recline with earphones and eyeshades. At some point the second LSD dose was given me. This phase was generally associated with impatience. I had been given instructions lest there be pain, fear or other difficulties. I was ready to try out my ability to face the unknown ahead of me, and to triumph over any obstacles. I was ready, but except for the physical sensations of awkwardness, and some drowsiness, nothing was happening.

At about this time, it seems, I fused with the music and was transported on it. So completely was I one with the sound that when the particular melody or record stopped, however, momentarily, I was alive to the pause, eagerly awaiting the next lap in the journey. A delightful game was being played. What was coming next? Would it be powerful, tender, dancing, or somber? I felt at these times as though I were being teased, but so nicely, so gently. I wanted to laugh in sheer appreciation—these responses, regardless of where I had just been, how sad or how awed. And as soon as the music began I was off again. Nor do I remember all the explorations.

Mainly I remember two experiences. I was alone in a timeless world with no boundaries. There was no atmosphere; there was no color, no imagery, but there may have been light. Suddenly, I recognized that I was a moment in time, created by those before me and in turn the creator of others. This was my moment, and my major function had been completed. By being born, I had given meaning to my parents' existence.

Again in the void, alone without the time-space boundaries. Life reduced itself over and over again to the least common denominator. I cannot remember the logic of the experience, but I became poignantly aware that the core of life is love. At this moment I felt that I was reaching out to the world—to all people—but especially to those closest to me. I wept long for the wasted years, the search for identity in false places, the neglected opportunities, the emotional energy lost in basically meaningless pursuits.

Many times, after respites, I went back, but always to variations on the same themes. The music carried me, and sustained me.

Occasionally, during rests, I was aware of the smell of peaches. The rose was nothing to the fruit. The fruit was nectar and ambrosia (life), the rose a beautiful flower only.

When I finally was given a nectarine, it was the epitome of subtle, succulent flavor.

As I began to emerge, I was taken outdoors to a fresh, rain swept world. Members of the department welcomed me and I felt not only joy for myself but for having been able to use the experience these people who cared wanted me to have. I felt very close to a large group of people.

Later, as members of my family came, there was a closeness that seemed new. That night, at home, my parents came, too. All noticed a change in me. I was radiant, they said. I seemed at peace, they said. I felt that way too. What has changed for me? I am living now, and being. I can take it as it comes. Some of my physical symptoms are gone. The excessive fatigue, some of the pains. I still get irritated occasionally and yell. I am still me, but more at peace. My family senses this and we are closer. All who know me well say that this has been a good experience.

MMPI's were administered to Patient D–1 one week prior and two weeks subsequent to her LSD session. The retesting indicated a significant reduction on the depression scale and a general lessening of pathological signs. She returned to work and appeared in relatively good spirits. Five weeks after the date of the session, upon the sudden development of ascites, the patient was rehospitalized. She died quietly three days later.

Investigation of the utility of psychedelic therapy with terminal patients is continuing with the collaboration of staff at the Sinai Hospital in Baltimore, Maryland.

CONCLUSION

Clinical studies have now been in progress at Spring Grove for over three years; nearly two hundred patients have been treated. We have been impressed by the relatively small number of *sequelae* that have been associated with this treatment approach. In our experience, we have found that psychedelic therapy is able to reach classes of patients who are refractory to conventional psychotherapy. It appears to be more effective and to require less time than conventional treatment. The hazards of this treatment form, when it is implemented by trained personnel, do not appear either special or unusual.

In conclusion, it should be emphasized that LSD is *not* conceived to have any inherent beneficial effects, *i.e.,* its use is different from that of other drugs or chemotherapeutic agents. LSD affects the brain of man in widespread and unusual ways, many of which are irrelevant to its therapeutic use (the production of so-called hallucinations, *etc.*). The history of experimental work with this compound has abundantly indicated that beneficial results do not occur from its mere administration—in fact, the indication is quite clear that without therapeutic intent, preparation and management, administration of the drug to human subjects is definitely dangerous. The therapeutic potential of LSD depends primarily on its ability to activate in the patient a period of intense emotionality while still allowing for control, direction and guidance by the therapist. It is the sequence of psychological experience upon which the therapeutic intent and structuring is focussed. The analogy that we have sometimes used to try to convey the role of LSD in therapy is that of a scalpel in surgical intervention: the scalpel is helpful, but without the skilled surgeon it is merely a dangerous instrument.

REFERENCES

Abramson, H. A. Lysergic acid diethylamide (LSD-25) as an adjunct to psychotherapy. *J. Psychology,* 1955, *39*: 127.

Abramson, H. A. The use of LSD in psychotherapy. In Josiah Macy, Jr., *Transactions of a conference.* New York: Foundation Press, 1960.

Busch, A. K., and Johnson, W. C. Lysergic acid diethylamide (LSD-25) as an aid in psychotherapy. *Dis. Nerv. Syst.,* 1950, *11*: 204.

James, W. *Varieties of Religious Experience.* London: Longmans, Green, 1906.

Kast, E. Pain and LSD-25: a theory of attenuation of anticipation. In D. Solomon (ed.), *LSD.* New York: Putnam, 1964.

Leuner, H., and Holfeld, H. Psychotherapy under the influence of the hallucinogens. *The Physicians' Panorama,* 1964, *2*: 13.

Ling and Buckman. The use of lysergic acid in individual psychotherapy. *Proc. Roy. Soc. Med.,* 1960, *53*: 927.

Masters, R. E., and Houston, J. *The Varieties of Psychedelic Experience.* New York: Holt, Rinehart, 1966.

Osmond, H. A review of the clinical effects of psychotomimetic agents. *Ann. N. Y. Acad. Sci.*, 1957, *66*: 418.

Sandison, R. A. Psychological aspects of the LSD treatment of the neuroses. *J. Ment. Sci.*, 1954, *100*: 508.

Sandison, R. A., Spencer, A. M., and Whitelaw, J. D. A. The therapeutic value of lysergic acid diethylamide in mental illness. *J. Ment. Sci.*, 1954, *100*: 491.

Sandison, R. A., and Whitelaw, J. D. A. Further studies in the therapeutic value of lysergic acid diethylamide in mental illness. *J. Ment. Sci.*, 1957, *103*: 332.

Savage, C. Lysergic acid diethylamide (LSD-25): a clinical-psychological study. *Am. J. Psychiat.*, 1952, *108*: 898.

Tiebout, H. Ego factors in surrender in alcoholism. *Quart. J. Studies Alc.*, 1954, *15*: 610.

3   The Abuse of LSD

By DONALD B. LOURIA

LYSERGIC acid diethylamide (LSD) has been extensively studied experimentally and used to good advantage in a limited number of clinical circumstances (Hoffer, 1965; Baker, 1964). For the most part, however, it is now used illicitly under non-medical aegis for hedonistic or pseudo-religious purposes. I shall discuss briefly four facets of illicit use—the prevalence of abuse, the nature of untoward reactions, the effects of irresponsible publicity and the relation of LSD to other hallucinogenic agents.

THE PREVALENCE OF ILLICIT USE

Unfortunately, no accurate data are available. Imprecise studies by the Medical Society of the County of New York (*N.Y. Medicine,* 1966) and by the magazine *Seventeen* (Lake, 1966) suggest that the incidence of abuse among young people does not exceed 1%. McGlothlin and Cohen's and Goldstein's experiences are consistent with these estimates (McGlothlin and Cohen, 1965; Goldstein, 1966). Berkowitz is quoted as finding that hallucinogen abuse involves some 1% to 2% of the population at a large Midwestern university (Berkowitz, 1966). Blum, studying a population in an area where drug use was known to be endemic, found that 3.5% of one group had tried LSD (Blum, 1966). (An indication that this figure is higher than one might expect in a broader sample is the observation that 4% of the sample had tried heroin.) Pearlman, in a careful study of college students in New York City, found that 2.5% of senior students had tried LSD at least once (Pearlman, in personal communication).

Balanced against these figures are unbuttressed statements that 10% to 15% of college students use LSD (Leary, 1966*a*). The higher figure, used by one of the leading proponents of widespread use of LSD, has been publically retracted (Leary, 1966*b*). It thus appears that abuse is limited to a small percentage of young persons, probably between 1% and 3%. Certainly there is no evidence that illicit use is more prevalent, and in point of fact the figure may well be less than 1%.

Two additional points should be stressed. First, the overwhelming majority of those currently using LSD illicitly do so on only one to three occasions. However, chronic use or habituation, now infrequent, is increasing.

Second, there appears to be some evidence of a reduction in LSD abuse in areas in which its use has been endemic. For example, at Bellevue Hospital in New York City the admission rate for persons with LSD-induced psychosis dropped 50% in late 1966, as compared to the figures for early and middle 1966. Whether this represents a valid trend or a transient but unsustained decrease is not clear. It is also certain that the reduction is not uniform, if anything the problem appears to be increasing in certain areas of California.

UNTOWARD REACTIONS

Among normals who are given LSD under medical aegis after careful screening, few serious reactions occur (estimated at 0.08%: Cohen, 1964). The adverse reaction rate is considerably higher in patients given LSD as an adjunct to psychotherapy— 0.2% to 2% developed prolonged psychiatric disorders, one in 830 attempted suicide and one in 2500 was successful (Cohen, 1964; Fink, Simeon, Hague and Itil, 1966).

The incidence of untoward reaction among those using LSD illicitly in uncontrolled circumstances is not known, but clearly it is substantially greater than that observed when LSD is prescribed for a specific medical or psychiatric illness.

Frosch, Robbins and Stern reported twenty-eight instances of LSD-induced psychosis requiring hospitalization (Frosch, Robbins and Stern, 1965). Ungerleider, Fisher and Fuller observed seventy cases, twenty-five of which were severe enough to necessitate hospitalization; and seventeen of these twenty-five required more than one month of in-patient treatment (Ungerleider, Fisher and Fuller, 1966). Similar series have been reported by Goddard (Goddard, 1966).

Said Dr. Sidney Cohen in May of 1966 (Cohen, 1966) regarding his experiences: "For the past six years I have been concerned about the possible adverse effects of the drug. Reports on more than 25,000 LSD or mescaline ingestions by some 5,000 subjects or patients were obtained. My report says that in those instances where LSD is given to preselected individuals under proper controls with adequate screening and protection, that the evidence of side effects is indeed a rarity. It is not fair to use this report to state that LSD is, therefore, a safe drug. On the contrary this report must be sharply distinguished from the complications which follow its indiscriminate use. During the past three years I have seen seventy-eight people who have taken LSD under uncontrolled, random, frivolous conditions and who have had prolonged difficulties. During the past few months one in every seven admissions to one small non-Veterans-Administration Neuropsychiatric Hospital is for LSD-precipitated disturbances."

Dr. Cohen and others list the following adverse reactions to LSD: (a) schizophrenic reactions; (b) a prolonged frightening LSD-like state; (c) chronic intoxication in children who took LSD inadvertently; (d) paranoid reactions; (e) psychotic depressions; (f) chronic anxiety reactions; (g) antisocial behavior; (h) convulsions; (i) dyssocial behavior; (j) acting out of homosexual impulses; (k) acting out of suicidal tendencies.

Our own experience at Bellevue Hospital covers some 130 in-patients observed over an eighteen-month period. Each was admitted for LSD-induced psychosis or LSD-caused exacerbation of an established psychiatric disorder. All had ingested the drug in uncontrolled circumstances, five having been given LSD without their knowledge. Since the drug was taken illicitly (usually on sugar cubes), there was no way of estimating the actual dosage, nor could the possibility be excluded that the psychosis might in part be ascribed to other drugs inadvertently ingested with the LSD. One hundred fourteen charts of patients were carefully reviewed. Of these patients, 88.4% were Caucasian, which fact clearly shows that LSD abuse does not occur among the groups that use heroin and cocaine. Of the latter, at least 70% are Negro, Puerto Rican or Mexican (U.S. Treasury report, 1966). Indeed, in New York City approximately 25% of the populace are Negro or

Puerto Rican, but only 12% of those hospitalized for LSD-induced psychosis were of these ethnic origins.

The average age was twenty-three years with a range of fifteen to forty-three. During recent months, more persons than previously have been more than thirty years of age, but illicit LSD use appears to be predominantly a disease of the young. Two-thirds of the patients were men.

Despite statements of proponents of widespread LSD use to the contrary, the drug can induce violent behavior: 12.3% entered with uncontrolled, aggressive tendencies or behavior, and 8.6% attempted either homicide or suicide. For example, one patient was apprehended because he attempted to kill the young child of his mistress, and another jumped in front of a train under the influence of LSD-induced auditory hallucinations.

Almost three-quarters of the 114 had taken LSD on only one to three occasions, but the psychosis in some instances occurred only after forty or more ingestions.

One-third of the patients had a history of overt underlying psychopathology, either neurosis or compensated psychosis. In most instances the background data were so meagre that it may well be that the percentage of those with major underlying personality abnormalities was in fact substantially greater.

Most patients recovered in forty-eight hours, but almost 16% had not recovered after two weeks and were eventually referred for potential long-term hospitalization. Of these, half had no prior psychiatric history.

Thus it appears clear that LSD can induce an acute psychosis in normals, which usually—but not always—disappears in forty-eight hours or less. Additionally, LSD can exacerbate a latent or compensated psychosis or neurosis, and this may result in long-term mental hospitalization. Whether one or a few LSD experiences can result in permanent mental derangement in a previously normal person remains unsettled.

The occupational history was obtained in sixty-eight cases and illustrates the varied background of the LSD users. Fifteen were in high school or college; eleven were classified as writers, artists, musicians or photographers; seven were employed as cooks, waiters or caterers and five as welders, carpenters or printers; five were models or dancers and eight teachers, physicians, pharmacists or engineers. Twelve were unemployed, and the occupations of the other five included housewife (2), beautician (1), typist (1) and rancher (1).

It has been frequently stated that LSD users are intelligent, middle-class or upper-class and intellectual; however, few firm data have been brought to bear on this issue. Blum is currently conducting a careful study in California, preliminary results of which have been published. Said Blum (Lerner, 1967): "The LSD users differed from other groups studied in that they were in more contact with physicians, had more experience with medication, were more dissatisfied with themselves and their work, reported themselves as more fearful of becoming dependent on drugs, reported themselves as having more cravings, being fearful of being exploited by others and sensitive to criticism. As a group I should say they were perhaps more troubled than any of the other people we saw."

Although there does appear to be a definite personality pattern underlying LSD use, the occupations of our patients as well as the studies of others suggest that use is diffusing throughout the various components of society.

Faced with the severe adverse reactions summarized above, the proponents of promiscuous LSD use have gone through sequential rationalizations. First, they denied that the hospitalized patients had taken LSD. When it became clear that such denial was untenable, they then insisted that the hospitalized patients had been mishandled. This failing, they have now adopted one of two approaches. Either they insist that the term psychosis is a conventional, colored word that is not applicable to any events following LSD ingestion, or they admit the psychosis, but absolve the LSD movement on the grounds that those who became psychotic should never have taken the drug. Neither the rationalizations, semantic gyrations or the attempts at exculpation can in any way lessen the heavy responsibility the LSD proselytizers bear for the growing number of severe, often prolonged, adverse reactions.

Four other points deserve emphasis. First, as pointed out by Frosch, Robbins and Stern (Frosch *et al.,* 1965), the visual and/or auditory hallucinations induced by LSD may return with startling intensity days, weeks or even months after the LSD was taken, despite the fact that no LSD or other hallucinogenic drug was taken in the interim. The recall of the experience in the absence of additional LSD is astounding in view of the minute amount of the drug that penetrates into the brain from the blood stream. The precise biochemical events that underlie this phenomenon of recall are not known.

Second, a review of the more recent admissions to Bellevue Hospital suggests that increasingly LSD is being taken by individuals with substantial psychiatric abnormalities, allegedly to illuminate the nature of their problems or to ameliorate them. This, of course, is precisely the patient group in which self-medication with LSD is inordinately dangerous.

Third, there is increasing evidence that subtle LSD-induced aberrations related to chronic abuse may in the long run exceed the damages inflicted acutely by the drug. Those who use frequently or chronically almost inevitably withdraw from society and enter into a solipsistic, negativistic existence, in which LSD is not merely an experience in the totality of living, but rather becomes syononymous with life itself. These individuals, colorfully described by their *confrères* as "acid-heads," engage perpetually in drug-induced orgies of introspection and are no longer constructive, active members of society. Often they withdraw not only from society but also from meaningful familial ties. Were the numbers of such individuals to increase markedly, such a group could constitute a real threat to the functioning of our society.

Fourth, the number of deaths attributed to jumping or falling out windows after ingesting LSD is clearly increasing despite widespread publicity given to these dramatic illustrations of lethal adverse reactions.

EFFECTS OF IRRESPONSIBLE PUBLICITY

There can be little doubt that the communications media bear a heavy responsibility for the spread of LSD abuse. Over and over they have emphasized the ecstasies and hedonistic values of LSD and underemphasized its enormous dangers. All too frequently sensationalism rather than facts and a balanced approach have characterized their efforts. At times reporters have carefully researched the dangers of LSD and then deliberately ignored or minimized them in the published articles.

Since virtually every major magazine, newspaper and television network has examined the LSD phenomenon, these uncritical and distorted reports have reached a large number of susceptible young persons. In every group of high-school or college students, there are some individuals who would never take LSD, some who could not be prevented from trying it and others, usually the majority, who are potentially susceptible to the inadvertent blandishments of the communications media. It is the latter group that is most likely to be harmed by such irresponsible publicity.

The most recent claim that terrifying LSD experiences can be immediately aborted and treated successfully with certain tranquillizers is the latest example of unsubstantiated reports being transmuted into valid facts and transmitted to the public. It is indeed true that under *controlled* circumstances administration of chlorpromazine, together with other supportive measures, *may* abort untoward reactions, but these ministrations are less likely to be successful in uncontrolled situations. Indeed, at Bellevue Hospital, patients are treated routinely with chlorpromazine, but this has not prevented one in six from requiring prolonged hospitalization. Similarly no tranquillizer helps the individual who in a sudden panic jumps out a window or in front of a train. Yet these reports, given wide publicity by an eager press, are being used to justify indiscriminate use of LSD.

Perhaps the most reprehensible and misleading statement regarding LSD is the claim that it is a potent aphrodisiac (Leary, 1966a). This claim is made by the avowed proselytizers, and more than any other single statement is effective in recruiting new converts to the LSD cult. LSD proponents insist that sexual relations under the influence of LSD are a spectacular, unmatched experience. They, of course, neglect to mention that the overwhelming majority of those taking LSD have no interest in sex, preferring their solipsistic trance, and that others who have taken LSD and attempted intercourse have found it impossible to consummate. Furthermore, the person responsible for the statement, when specifically challenged on this point in a public debate in the fall of 1966, said that the statement was misinterpreted and that he in fact meant that LSD induces love in its most ethereal sense, but has no beneficial effect on casual or promiscuous physical sexual behavior (Leary, 1966*b*).

Yet the myth, almost surely deliberately promulgated, will persist and will coax unsuspecting young people to try a drug that has the capacity to affect adversely their lives acutely, chronically or even permanently. The same myth has been utilized by proponents of marijuana, cocaine and the amphetamines. For those who would proselytize, sex is always better under the drug that they illicitly use.

There is, of course, an additional inducement for some to continue the publicity and to disseminate the myths. These individuals are involved in secondary gain, which takes the form either of personal notoriety or of monetary reward. The LSD proponents hawk their psychedelic wares in hard-cover books, paperbacks, pamphlets and speeches. Furthermore, they openly admit that there is virtually unlimited commercial applicability for the psychedelic movement; theatre shows, discothèques, cabarets, restaurants, motion pictures, *etc.* with psychedelic motif are providing handsome financial returns. For these entrepreneurs, the use of LSD *per se* is not mandatory, but the LSD mystique, together with the myths and the publicity, is a necessary component that reminds the audience that their money is being spent on a psychedelic experience that mimics the hedonistic effects of the drug. Inevitably, some of those who enjoy the non-drug psychedelic experience will be inveigled by the overt and surreptitious inducements to try the real thing. To quote Dr. Sidney Cohen: "Some of the young in mind who obtain the black market material will casually take it under dubious conditions and without the necessary controls. Sooner or later they will find themselves caught in the grip of pure horror. With LSD the kicks can go both ways" (Cohen, 1964).

THE ABUSE OF OTHER POTENT HALLUCINOGENS

LSD is only one of many moderately to markedly potent hallucinogenic agents. A small number are known in Europe, Asia and Africa, and Latin America is a veritable hallucinogenic cornucopia. Some of those currently available in the United States are listed in Table I. Of these, dimethyltryptamine (DMT) offers the greatest potential for widespread abuse, because it is the most readily manufactured. Usually smoked, it can also be snuffed, ingested or injected.

TABLE I
Potent Hallucinogens Illicitly Used in The United States

Lysergic acid diethylamide (LSD-25)
Psilocybin
Mescaline
Dimethyltryptamine (DMT)
Bufotenine
Hashish

A partial list of hallucinogens found in other parts of the world is shown in Table II on pages 46–48. For the most part these are used by primitive peoples in religious rites, in warfare, in tribal ceremonies, for purposes of divination or for transient escape from the deprivations and appalling poverty that characterize their daily existence. It seems unlikely that any of these will be directly used in the United States in their present forms, but the active components of some of them have been or will soon be defined chemically. These synthetic hallucinogens will then be available for illicit manufacture and indiscriminate use. This is in fact what happened with dimethyltryptamine and psilocybin; the former constitutes an active principle in several hallucinogenic substances of Latin America (see Table II), and the latter is an active component of the sacred hallucinogenic Mexican mushroom *Psilocybe mexicana*. In each case it was the synthetic drug rather than the naturally occurring agent that was illicitly used in the United States.

Thus LSD can be regarded only as one head of a psychedelic hydra; eliminate it, and we shall surely face other similar agents. The therapy for this abuse must consequently be general, not parochial, and must be multifaceted. If we as a society make the judgement, as indeed we must, that proliferation of these drugs and indiscriminate use of them under non-medical aegis are dangerous to the individual and potentially dangerous to society, then we have a right to demand appropriate controls.

The following would appear to be essential components of any attack on hallucinogen abuse:

a. Laws restricting supply by imposing severe penalties for illicit importation, manufacture or sale.

b. Laws making illegal possession a misdemeanor. This conceivably could merely drive LSD and similar drugs underground, make them more enticing and thus expand illicit use; however, it is more likely that such laws, combined with dissemination of knowledge about physical and mental risks, would persuade some potentially susceptible individuals to eschew use of potent and potentially dangerous hallucinogens.

c. Laws proscribing possession of precursors of hallucinogens such as LSD and mescaline. If lysergic acid and trimethoxyphenyl-acetonitrile were not available, the abuse of lysergic acid diethylamide or mescaline would almost surely decline. Of the currently used potent hallucinogens, only DMT is so easy to manufacture that its precursors could not be interdicted.

d. Education. Young people are, for the most part, eminently educable. Vigorous, continuous and impeccably honest education about the dangers of potent hallucinogens should do more than laws to reduce the numbers influenced by the psychedelic proselytizers.

e. Strengthening the family unit. It perhaps seems trite to emphasize that deterioration of the cohesiveness of the family unit has resulted in the presence in society of an increasing number of insecure, unhappy and confused young persons. Such individuals either do not have the strength to resist the lure of LSD or may actively seek the drug as a manifestation of inherent personality defects. Surely a strong and loving family unit is far more likely to produce young persons strong enough to separate wants from needs, to reject drug proselytizers and to seek constructive solutions to their problems. If the family unit is not revitalized, efforts at prevention by a combination of laws and education will surely be only partially successful.

TABLE II

Some Hallucinogens Used Throughout The World

	Substance	Active principle	Source	Major area of use	Purpose	How taken
1.	Glue	Toluene	Commercial	U. S. A.	Euphoria	Sniff
2.	Gas vapor	Trichlorethylene, cyclohexanol, ethylene dichloride, toluene	Commercial	U. S. A.	Euphoria, hedonism	Sniff
3.	Cannabis (marijuana, bhang, dagga, kif, hashish)	Cannabinol	C. sativa (C. indica)	World-wide	Pleasure	Smoke, drink, food
4.	Peyote	Mescaline (epinephrine-like)	Cactus, L. williamsii	U. S. A., Mexico	Religious, ritual, hedonism	Chew, drink (can inject mescaline)
5.	Psilocin, psilocybin	Serotonin derivatives	Basiodiomycete P. mexicana (teonanactyl)	Mexico, U. S. A.	Religious, ritual	Oral
6.	Ololiuqui	Lysergic acid	Rivea corymbosa	Mexico	Pleasure, ritual	Chew seeds

TABLE II (*Continued*)

Substance	Active principle	Source	Major area of use	Purpose	How taken
7. Pituri	Scopolamine	Potato-like shrub Dubiosia hopwoodii	Australia	Relief from thirst, strength	Chew mixed with ashes or acacia wood
8. Caapi (Yahee) (ayahuasca)	Banisterine	Vine-Banisteria caapi	South America (Columbia, Brazil)	Whipping ceremony, aphrodisiac, prophecy	Drink
9. Datura	Stramonium, scopolamine, hyoscyamine	Datura sp.	Mexico, Equador, Peru, Colombia	Aphrodisiac, religious, magic	Drink
10. Ibogaine	Harmine (banisterine)	Plant-iboga tabernanthe	Africa	Stimulant, ordeal ceremony	Chew
11. Fly agaric	Muscarine, bufotenine	Basidiomycete A. muscaria	Siberia	Pleasure, relief from environment	Drink, chew

TABLE II (*Continued*)

	Substance	Active principle	Source	Major area of use	Purpose	How taken
12.	Yakee epina	Myristicine, DMT, bufotenine	Virola sp. (nutmeg)	Venezuela, Brazil, Colombia	Religious, magic	Snuff
13.	Vinho de Juremena	Nigarine (dimethyl-tryptamine)	Mimosa hostilis	South America	Religious, magic	Drink
14.	Cohoba (yopo, niopo)	Bufotenine, DMT	Piptadenia peregrina	Colombia, Venezuela	Magic, warfare, orgiastic	Snuff
15.	—	—	Saliva divinarum	Mexico	Religious, magic	Chew leaves

REFERENCES

Baker, E. F. W. The use of lysergic acid diethylamide in psychotherapy. *Canada Med. Assoc. J.*, 1964, *91*:1200.

Berkowitz, S. Chapter 5. In W. Young and J. Hixson, *LSD on campus.* New York: Dell, 1966.

Blum, R. In *The Proceedings of the Committee on Government Operations of the United States Senate of the 89th Congress, 24-26 May 1966*, p. 115. Washington, D. C.: U. S. Gov't Printing Office, 1966.

Cohen, S. *The Beyond Within: The LSD Story.* New York: Atheneum, 1964.

Cohen, S. In *The Proceedings of the Committee on Government Operations of the United States Senate of the 89th Congress, 24-26 May 1966*, p. 144. Washington, D. C.: U. S. Gov't Printing Office, 1966.

Fink, M., Simeon, J., Hague, W., and Itil, T. Prolonged adverse reactions to LSD in psychotic subjects. *Arch. Gen. Psychiat.*, 1966, *15*:450.

Frosch, W. A., Robbins, E. S., and Stern, M. Untoward reactions to lysergic acid diethylamide (LSD) resulting in hospitalization. *New Engl. J. Med.*, 1965, *273*: 1235.

Goddard, J. In *The Proceedings of the Committee on Government Operations of the United States Senate of the 89th Congress, 24-26 May 1966*, p. 144. Washington, D. C.: U. S. Gov't Printing Office, 1966.

Goldstein, R. *One in Seven—Drugs on Campus.* New York: Walker, 1966.

Hoffer, A. D-lysergic acid diethylamide (LSD), a review of its present status. *Clin. Pharm. and Therapeutics*, 1965, *6*: 183.

Lake, A. Drugs, a student report. *Seventeen*, Sept., 1966, p. 170.

Leary, T. Interview. *Playboy*, Sept., 1966*a*, p. 93.

Leary, T. In a talk at Muhlenberg College in December of 1966(*b*).

Lerner, M. LSD spelled out. *Mademoiselle*, Jan., 1967, p. 52.

McGlothlin, W. H., and Cohen, S. The use of hallucinogenic drugs among college students. *Amer. J. Psychiat.*, 1965, *122*: 572.

Pearlman, S. In personal communication.

Ungerleider, J. T., Fisher, D. D., and Fuller, M. The dangers of LSD. *JAMA*, 1966, *197*:389.

The dangerous drug problem. *N. Y. Medicine*, 20 July, 1966, *XXII*: 14.

Traffic in opium and other dangerous drugs. A report by the United States Treasury Bureau of Narcotics. Washington, D. C.: U. S. Gov't Printing Office, 1966.

4   First Discussion

The Moderator: I am going to ask a question about sexual behavior, because I think that the implications of what we have heard today on this matter are rather important, insofar as some of the colloquial passing on of information about LSD is concerned.

What I have heard in discussions with people who have used LSD is this: that the sexual effects may not be present during the session itself, but there is what might be called a post-experience effect. I didn't prepare to speak about this, so I don't have a reference for you; but it is my understanding that one of the leading proponents of the usage of LSD has said that any woman who takes LSD in the presence of a man is forever in love with him. But I'd like the panel—a volunteer—to respond to this notion that a post-experience may be what is being talked about.

Dr. Louria: I'll respond. It's a lot of junk. I want to make sure that we're all clear about this aspect. I didn't mean to imply in my remarks that somebody who takes LSD and has intercourse during or after the experience can't have a great response to it. The fact of the matter is that that may happen; but it really is not a frequent phenomenon. If anybody starts giving out or taking LSD with that specifically in mind, he is going to be sorely disappointed. As far as the drug's being beneficial to sexual enjoyment afterwards, the statement about its being taken in the presence of a woman who will always be in love with you is ridiculous. In the first place, we have enough trouble without people always falling in love with us. But in any case, that doesn't happen. Whatever happens after LSD, if somebody has taken it, is colored by the fact of his having taken LSD. If you go to Sweden, they'll tell you exactly the same thing about phenmetrazine, an amphetamine-like compound that is now the big kick in Sweden. In Stockholm, for example, there are four thousand phenmetrazine *habitués* in a relatively small population, a phenomenal number. And if you talk to people who are strong advocates of pot, they'll tell you the same thing about pot. I think that it's whatever you take. If you decide that you want to take it and that it makes you feel good, then everything else thereafter falls under its panoply—you know, it's wonderful.

The moderator: Do you want to ask questions of each other?

Mr. Barron: I have a comment. I would agree also that that statement, given as unqualified generalization, is simply nonsense. But I do think that there are cases—some of which I know—of a man and woman who have taken a psychedelic drug together falling in love. But as far as its being either invariable or very frequent, no. The answer is no.

A member of the audience: I couldn't help noticing that you, Dr. Louria, seem to dismiss quite flippantly some of the most profound aspects that Mr. Barron spoke of. I wonder if your perception is colored by the fact that your experience with LSD comes from seeing it in your work.

The moderator: The question is whether Dr. Louria's opinions on LSD are a result of his experience in a medical setting, primarily at Bellevue, where he sees LSD at its worst.

Dr. Louria: You are absolutely correct. My sole interest, aside from deciding whether it will benefit my wife and dog, is trying to decide whether or not it's a public health problem. So, of course, we see it in its worst aspects. But from those aspects, by knowing trouble and abuse and complications, we can get a reasonably good idea what the general risk is. If the general risk is large, then we've got to campaign against it as a public health problem. And that's exactly what we are doing. I don't for a minute mean to imply that somebody taking LSD can't have an absolutely gorgeous experience. Of course it is possible, but that doesn't in any way alter the basic fact that it is a very substantial public health problem. The last time Leary and I talked about this, what he finally said after we had a long and bitter debate, was: "You, in the medical profession, are trying to control my inner self, and it's none of your damn business." And I agreed with him. Of course, we don't care. We are not trying to make a martyr of Leary. We couldn't care less what he does. If he wants to go out to Millbrook and take a gallon of LSD every day of his life, that's his privilege; and we wouldn't be here talking to this group or to any other group that wants us to talk to them if that were the situation. But that isn't the situation. What happens is that these people, he and his colleagues, having taken LSD, become avid public proponents, and that is entirely different from having their own pleasures, their own hallucinations in private. Once they do become proponents, then they are forcing the LSD problem into the public sphere, where very often there are severe reactions to it. And that's why we're involved. Of course you're right. We are looking at it from one point of view. But I think that we have to.

A member of the audience: Do you feel that perhaps there is something valuable in the preventive-medicine aspect of LSD and that perhaps the Public Health Service could be looking into this aspect with a little bit more open arms? The second part of the question is why is legislation necessary when education could be intensified without the unfortunate side-effects of driving the material underground by legislative activities and creating a market there?

The moderator: Two-part question. The first part is, essentially, why hasn't society investigated the possible preventive-medicine aspects of LSD usage?

Dr. Louria: My answer to that is that I think it is worth investigating. We proposed that in our very first statement opposing the indiscriminate use of LSD, proposed that research be markedly increased and at all levels. That includes sociological research—what would happen to a person given, say, 10 μg of LSD a day in his productivity, in his ability to enjoy hobbies, *etc.* The unfortunate answer is that currently not enough funds are available. We would like to see more. I think that you are right there. The people who talk the loudest are least willing to undertake such a study. Mr. Leary, for example, will not. He and I have talked this over, and he has talked about it publicly, and his answer is that we would compel him to have a competent psychiatrist attached to his program—not running it, attached to it—because of the potential medical danger. He and his colleagues refuse to accept that. They say that they want this under totally uncontrolled circumstances, that any home that they designate as a shrine shall be a shrine, and that any person who wants LSD should have LSD, without any controls or any analysis of his background or personality characteristics. And they are even talking about a future in which people will be walking into lunch-time clinics, taking their LSD and then walking out again. Now, if that's what he means by experimenting with LSD, then we are implacably and permanently opposed to it. What you propose, expansion of research at all levels, including finding out what it could do on a careful outpatient basis, is exactly what we are for, just as long as it is under proper aegis.

The same member of the audience: I didn't propose, necessarily, tighter controls, as you seem to be getting at in your extreme statement at the end. Or perhaps it's not extreme. It seems to me, though, that there could be a little more trust of individuals by the government.

Dr. Louria: No. The answer to that is that no medical society would ever condone it. I wouldn't trust the people who are talking most about LSD under any conditions. I want this stuff controlled by people who really know what they're doing and are willing to do this right. For goodness sake, that kind of study—that trust study, give it out and see what it will do on a preventive basis—you do that for twenty years and twenty years from now you won't know any more about what it does. I want people like Dr. Kurland to study it more. If we had a hundred more studies like his expanded on a whole variety of levels, sociological, psychological, disciplined studies, carefully evaluated, why then five years from now we would really be able to say what this drug can do and what it cannot.

The same member of the audience: Are you fostering such study?

Dr. Louria: Yes.

The moderator: There was a second part to the question. The second part of the question is why adopt laws that drive drug usage underground? And lead to the difficult situation that became apparent during Prohibition? I am not sure that this question will be maximally answered now, though it might be during the evening session. However, if someone would like to speak to it, we can anticipate the evening session.

Dr. Louria: Well, I can give a simple answer—because we are for the laws. There is not a need for LSD; we have an established escape mechanism in society, namely, alcohol, which you know you can't prohibit, but this is not a matter of physiological need. It is a matter of want. Under those conditions, we are perfectly convinced that, if necessary, laws can be effective. With LSD, for example, I don't have any question that if our laws are implemented, the use of

LSD will be markedly reduced, and all the evidence that we now have says that this is true.

In September of 1966, for example, they not only proscribed LSD, but its precursor as well. And as you learned this morning, you can't make LSD in just any laboratory. I don't have any question at all that by laws we can markedly reduce the use of LSD. You have to make a judgement sometimes as to what a society is going to permit and not to permit. And I think that with drugs, especially when there is such enormous proliferation, society must decide for its own good what it will permit to be used indiscriminately and what it will not. For example, if we just say "Don't use LSD," what right have you to say "Don't use amphetamines?" All you want. Or barbiturates. Or heroin. Or cocaine. Where do you stop?

A member of the audience: I'd like to address a question to Dr. Louria. It really seems clear, as Dr. Louria presented the major problem in all sorts of areas such as risk-to-pleasure, that really there's been a lack of hard information about what this ratio is in comparison to what the ratio is for other drugs that are now prescribed and open on the market. I don't mean to suppose that you can make a comparison in relation to alcohol or a barbiturate or heroin, but certainly there is a relationship, and the government has certainly decided in one instance that the ratio is much to the bad, and therefore this is outlawed. And in other instances it has decided it is much to the good. I wonder if you can specify what this ratio is and then suggest a possible way of adjusting this ratio, not just outlawing LSD, but changing the ratio. Dr. Kurland, is there some way that the ratio of risk-to-pleasure can be lessened so that the amount of good is, in fact, enhanced?

The moderator: Many drugs that involve risk are available for prescription and for purchase without prescription. Obviously, society or government, which is the instrument of society, makes decisions about the point at which the pleasure-to-risk ratio is thought to be so great or so bad that it legislates against the use of that drug, making it unavailable. The questioner was asking how that ratio is determined and if something can be done to make the ratio more favorable?

Mr. Barron: One or two things should be said here, because the question itself, in a sense, omits an important consideration. The phrase pleasure-to-risk ratio may not be the appropriate phrase. Why not utility-to-risk ratio? For example, a very dangerous article, besides firearms, that we use commonly is the automobile, and we hear no talk of prohibiting the automobile, because the automobile is so very useful to us. Yet, it wreaks considerable carnage.

Dr. Louria: It's a thing, not a drug.

Mr. Barron: Are you saying that a drug is intrinsically different? I'm saying that it's a useful object.

Dr. Louria: I could give a lot of reasons for doing that. In the first place, your question asks if the ratio is known? The answer is absolutely not. But we know it is a relatively substantial one, compared to that of drugs that you can buy on the market. Second, there is no known medical use for LSD now, no known condition in which you can prescribe it on an out-patient basis and have it be beneficial. So there's even more reason not just to permit it to be given. We don't give any of the medical drugs with such potential danger just willy-nilly. And, as you know, we are going just the other way; we are going too far. Now we are going to proscribe cough medicine containing codeine, which I think is too much restriction, because the dangers there are very small.

Mr. Barron: I want to comment further on this, because now I am beginning to understand why the Leary-Louria debate is going on. You speak as though drugs were somehow just the province of the medical profession. Many of these substances are naturally occurring substances, available to anyone who lives on the earth.

Dr. Louria: Drugs that are synthesized and used for medicinal purposes are the province of the medical profession by and large. There are a few exceptions to this. Alcohol is obviously one. But our society has made a judgement that they are, and we are not about to go back on that judgement. If so, let's give all the drugs out to the general public—digitalis, penicillin, LSD, heroin. All drugs that are synthesized, if they are dangerous, have, unfortunately, to be controlled. That's why we have a Food and Drug Administration. When you have cars, you have to have traffic laws. It's not the car that's so dangerous intrinsically. It is the way it is used. And that's why we have laws to regulate it. It's not the drug that is necessarily so dangerous. It's dangerous if it's taken in a dangerous manner. Same thing is true about laws. There is the old

biblical statement "Laws are good so long as they are treated law-
fully." I think that the same is true of our drugs. Drugs are good
so long as they are used sensibly. I think that you've got to control
certain things, and dangerous drugs happen to be one that we've
decided that we are going to control. And LSD is one of them.
That's all there is to it.

A member of the audience: I think it's probably more truthful
to regard the question of the use of LSD as something of a cultural
problem. We can't move culture back to something that so many
persons seem to demonstrate is no longer viable for them. You
cannot go back to what has become demonstrably more and more
unacceptable. I was wondering if we should seriously consider
strengthening the kind of institution that the members of our culture are choosing to abandon in larger numbers?

The moderator: The questioner, as I understand him, is saying
that many of the normative aspects of society, the values of society,
upon which the questioner believes Dr. Louria's statements are
based, are becoming obsolete and that there are many factors
within our society that no longer support the authoritarian, if you
will, viewpoint that he is presenting. He has been asked to comment on the adaptability, essentially, of his viewpoint to these
changes within society.

Dr. Louria: All right. In answer to your question, for some of
the drugs, this wouldn't, of course, apply. Let's restrict it to LSD,
because when I talked about slums, that was related to heroin. We
can do something about slums, although society will not, at least
now, do what is necessary. Either we do something about slums, or
we don't get rid of the heroin problem. It's that simple. There we
could knock out 80% of the problem if we'd eliminate just the
slums in New York City. The heroin users might all turn to alcohol
or to LSD, but at least they wouldn't be taking heroin.

About the other, well, the point that I obviously was not articulate enough on was that if we cannot get at the cause, namely,
insecurity in the individual, then obviously our controls of drug
abuse will depend on a combination of education and laws, more
education, if possible, and fewer laws. But this doesn't mean that I
don't think that we can't go back to strengthening the family unit.
I don't want to get into this problem, because it's too involved, and
I don't want to monopolize the discussion, but the history of

western civilization is naturally cyclic. Just because we have had thirty years of deterioration of the family unit does not mean that the family unit is dying. According to what has happened in prior western civilizations, in Greece and in Rome, for examples, there's every evidence that the family unit will again strengthen as the cycle swings.

Second, I think that we can, at will, make a more disciplined society if we want to do so. I think that we have just gone too far in allowing permissiveness in the family and in the colleges. I think that this overly permissive attitude can readily be changed if we are willing to take a firm stand. And I think that we could make persons more secure and less predisposed to drugs if we understand what makes them this way, as Blum will help us do, and if we do something early in their lives to correct it. For example, there are those people who feel that they have no close ties with others or with the community. I think that we could do something in our schools toward teaching them about community participation. I think there are many ways to approach this, though I agree with your basic point that it may be very difficult. All I would like to see us do is to take a crack at it.

A member of the audience: I would like to ask Dr. Kurland if he has data on the complications after any therapy that has cured neurotic symptoms? I feel that it would not be a factor of LSD's raising the I.Q., but rather of its altering the neurotic symptoms.

The moderator: The question is if other methods of treatment of neuroses that also result in the alleviation of the neuroses lead to the elevation of the score on the I.Q. test? Dr. Kurland?

Dr. Kurland: The question is a pertinent one, and it was thought of in the designs set up for the controlled studies. We do have a control group, some of whom are responding very nicely to other types of treatment, and we are considering this possibility. In due time, perhaps a year or so from now, this data will certainly be analyzed to see if there is a statistical difference between those who improve on LSD and those who improve under other forms of treatment and if this is related to changes in the neurotic pattern. This has all been considered, but, unfortunately, you are a year ahead of me with your question.

A member of the audience: Dr. Louria, as I understand the statistics that you presented, 1% of the population of New York

City is using LSD; and all those who use LSD and have bad reactions come to Bellevue Hospital and are admitted, rather than treated as out-patients. It seems to me that 2% of the users, roughly, are getting into Bellevue.

The moderator: As I understand the question, it is what percentage of users of LSD in New York City are actually being admitted to Bellevue?

Dr. Louria: I can't answer that, and neither can anybody else. The figure that we have of the number of people using LSD is not related to the general population, but to the young, generally the college-age group. The surveys have been done among young people, the people who come to Bellevue Hospital and are sent home, and they are, depending on the month of the year. There may be large or small numbers, otherwise, who are automatically excluded. We don't know what percentage, and neither does anybody else—what percentage of those using LSD under non-medical aegis get into trouble from it. All we do know is that the figure given of one in ten thousand, which is Mr. Leary's figure, cannot be right, because if that were true, on the Bellevue Hospital statistics alone, there would be one million LSD users in New York City, and obviously that's spurious. So the answer to your question is that we cannot go on their figure for LSD users in New York City, which, by the way, is about fifty thousand. That is the figure of Mr. Leary and his colleagues. Obviously, the one in ten thousand doesn't make any sense, but neither do our figures. All we can say is that we never saw LSD psychosis prior to two years ago, and now it's a major cause for hospitalization among young people.

A member of the audience: I understand that since the supply of LSD is illicit, the dosage and purity are probably not under rigorous quality control. I wonder if Dr. Louria would care to comment on the range of dosage discrepancies and impurities that he has found?

The moderator: The question is not about the pleasure-to-risk ratio in terms of mental illness, but just about the risk of dosages. Since all of the preparation now must be illicit, what are the ranges in dosage levels and in impurities contained in the commercially purchased LSD?

Dr. Louria: That's a very good point. The answer is that nobody knows what the dose is on any given cube. The measured doses range from 50 to 700 μg per cube. Somebody here, perhaps the F.D.A. representatives or one of the other panelists, will know what the impurities are. I don't have any idea, though everybody is well aware that impurities are on the cubes. You are absolutely correct.

A member of the audience: I'd like to address Mr. Barron. What did you feel about creativity and LSD?

The moderator: Mr. Barron has been asked to elaborate on the role of LSD in enhancement of creativity.

Mr. Barron: There has been, to my knowledge, only one study that could claim attention on the basis of the validity of measures used, a study by McGlothlin and Cohen. There was a difference of only marginal significance in improvement in originality and ideational fluency, two of the variables measured in this study. On the basis of that research one would say that no very dramatic increases occur. Probably the increment is just entirely marginal. This question is a little bit akin to the "Is LSD dangerous?" question. It's dangerous if the person is dangerous. And I think that it can serve certain kinds of users as a catalyst of imagination, individuals who are already disposed toward it and trained, painters, for example. I've seen some quite interesting productions that were based upon experiences that occurred when the individual had taken a psychedelic drug. For example, one composer of international reputation, taking psilocybin, spent all his time simply listening to music, though there wasn't any music being played. He heard it in himself and made it the basis for a symphonic composition, remembered it and wrote it down. The important thing about this case is that he had a prepared mind, a capacity already there, and the drug itself acted almost as a catalyst, intensifying reactions, perhaps speeding them up. This has to be appreciated, by the way, because sometimes a threshhold for a certain type of response is changed as a result of an experience, the very having of the experience; and the changed threshhold can result in having a memory of the experience that can be used again. In brief, what I would say is that there is no evidence of the hard sort that we hope to build up if research could continue unrestricted, but that there are enough anecdotal stories of composition as a result of insights gained under the experience to indicate that it may well have a catalytic effect.

5 LSD and Religious Experience

By WALTER N. PAHNKE

THE relationship between LSD and religious experience is an issue that is quite complex and needs careful analysis to avoid a loose and uncritical association. It would be misleading to assume that the experiences are automatically identical.

LSD-type drugs have been called by many names. In the early 1950's the term *psychotomimetic, i.e.,* psychosis-mimicking, was generally used; but this rather negatively loaded term was seen by some as being too narrow and limiting to accommodate the wide range of experiences being reported and observed. In 1957 Dr. Humphry Osmond (Osmond, 1957) proposed the term *psychedelic, i.e.,* mind-opening or mind-manifesting, to encompass the full range of positive and negative experiences that he had seen in his work with such drugs. Psychedelic will be the term used in this paper to refer to the unique class of LSD-type drugs.

In this discussion a survey will first be made of the various kinds of psychedelic experiences with an especial examination of the mystical type, and possible reasons for this variety will be mentioned. Then we shall look at some of the evidence that psychedelic mystical experiences occur at all and discuss whether or not they can be considered "religious." The LSD churches that have grown out of the evangelistic enthusiasm associated with LSD will also be examined along with their possible impact on individuals and society. Finally, the future prospects for the investigation and use of psychedelic drugs will be discussed.

Psychedelic experiences can be divided into five types: psychotic, psychodynamic, cognitive, aesthetic and psychedelic peak or mystical. These have been described elsewhere (Pahnke and Richards, 1966), and a brief description of each will suffice.

The *psychotic* experience is described as very intense, negative, dysphoric and hellish by those who have been through it. Characteristic elements include fear to the point of panic, paranoid distrust, delusions of suspicion or grandeur, toxic confusion, impairment of abstract reasoning, remorse, depression, isolation and/or somatic discomfort, all of which can be of monumental proportions. These words can perhaps be better illuminated by the following description written by a well-prepared subject who took LSD under medical supervision:

> Time itself seemed to have frozen. I was sick way down inside. I had lost trust in the doctor and the judgment of part of my own mind. The terrible thing was that I was going insane and the normal part of my mind knew this was taking place. I was two people in the same body. The one with the insane mind was pulling the one with the sane mind over on his side. I think I was 95% insane.
>
> Then things became even more confused and frightening. It seemed as if I had three minds, two that were insane and one perfectly normal. In other words, I was having the experience of having a front row seat watching myself who was insane.
>
> Faces now looked distorted, eyes were of a cruel expression, and they seemed to have the power of looking through me and my very thoughts. The least amount of noise sounded one hundred times louder. Everything I heard was driving me into a living hell. The doctor looked like the devil to me. He had tricked me.
>
> I didn't think either of us was sane now. As a matter of fact, I thought everyone was inhuman, and I would go through life in this situation and this would go on forever. There never even existed something as wonderful as death that could get me—body and mind—out of this horrible, unnatural life (Unger, 1964).

This account illustrates especially well the feeling of many people at some time during an LSD session that something has gone wrong and that they never will be the same again. Such feelings only increase the panic and hopelessness. Adequate preparation and skilled handling, however, do make a crucial difference in the outcome of most cases. In this particular instance, the patient was guided through an extremely frightening and unpleasant part of his experience to a very positive and helpful climax. Unfortunately, such a happy ending is quite uncertain in uncontrolled settings.

The second type of experience is the *psychodynamic,* in which material that had previously been unconscious or preconscious becomes vividly conscious. We see abreaction and catharsis in the reliving of traumatic incidents from the past or in the experiencing of symbolic material. The use of LSD in Europe employs what has been termed the psycholytic method, which emphasizes the uncovering of psychodynamic material. Suggestion certainly plays a role, because the patients of Freudian therapists produce incidents from the stages of psychosexual development, whereas archetypal symbols are often encountered by patients of Jungian therapists. Essential to this method, however, is the support and guidance of a skilled therapist, both while the patient is having the experience and while he is between drug sessions. A detailed description of the psycholytic method has now been published in the papers presented at an international LSD conference in 1965 (Abramson, 1967).

The third type of experience, the *cognitive,* is characterized by astonishingly lucid thought. The mind seems subjectively to be able to view things from a new perspective and to see the interrelationships of many levels or dimensions all at once. Such experiences usually occur when the drug effects are waning. The very existence of such states of mind led people to speculate that creativity research might be aided with psychedelic drugs. Harman and his co-workers (Harman, McKim, Mogar, Fadiman and Stolaroff, 1966) have already published a pilot study in which twenty-seven professionally employed males underwent a single moderate-dose psychedelic session in a small group setting. Each subject had a particular problem on which he could not obtain closure and hoped to gain some new perspective through the psychedelic experience. The setting was structured so that expectation was maximized, and the sessions were run with a minimum of interruption. The results in terms of problems actually solved were promising (9 out of 44 attempted problems yielded practical solutions), but not conclusive because of the lack of a control group. Certainly this is an area that merits further investigation.

The fourth type of experience is the *aesthetic.* Perhaps the reported increase in all sensory modalities is what attracts some people to take LSD for "kicks." These reports do not exaggerate. Fascinating changes in sensation and perception do occur: synaesthesia in which sounds can be "seen;" objects such as flowers or stones that appear to pulsate and become "alive;" ordinary things that seem imbued with great beauty; music that takes on an incredible emotional power; and visions of beautiful colors, intricate geometrical patterns, architectural forms, landscapes or almost anything imaginable.

The fifth type of experience is the focus of interest in this presentation and has been called by various names: *psychedelic peak, transcendental* or *mystical.* For the sake of this discussion we shall refer to it as the psychedelic mystical or experimental mystical experience. Its psychological characteristics have been described elsewhere (Pahnke, in unpublished thesis) and will be only briefly summarized here.

These characteristics, nine in number, were derived from a study of the literature of spontaneous mystical experiences reported throughout world history from almost all cultures and religions. In studying accounts of these strange, unusual experiences, an attempt was made to extract the universal psychological characteristics as free from interpretation as possible. Scientific evidence indicates that these universal characteristics derived from spontaneous mystical experiences also precisely describe experimental psychedelic ones.

The nine characteristics can be listed as follows:

1. *Unity* is a sense of cosmic oneness achieved through positive ego-transcendence. Although the usual sense of identity or ego fades away, consciousness and memory are not lost; instead, the person becomes very much aware of being part of a dimension much vaster and greater than himself. In addition to the route of the "inner world" where all external sense impressions are left behind, unity can also be experienced through the external world, so that a person reports that he feels a part of everything that is (*e.g.,* objects, other people, nature or the universe), or, more simply, that "all is one."

2. *Transcendence of time and space* means that the subject feels beyond past, present and future and beyond ordinary three-dimensional space in a realm of eternity or infinity.

3. *Deeply felt positive mood* contains the elements of joy, blessedness, peace and love to an overwhelming degree of intensity, often accompanied by tears.

4. *Sense of sacredness* is a non-rational, intuitive, hushed, palpitant response of awe and wonder in the presence of inspiring realities. The main elements are awe, humility and reverence, but the terms of traditional theology or religion need not necessarily be used in the description.

5. *The noetic quality,* as named by William James, is a feeling of insight or illumination that is felt on an intuitive, non-rational level and has a tremendous force of certainty and reality. This knowledge is not an increase in facts, but is a gain of insight about such things as philosophy of life or sense of values.

6. *Paradoxicality* refers to the logical contradictions that become apparent if descriptions are strictly analyzed. A person may realize that he is experiencing, for example, an "identity of opposites," yet it seems to make sense at the time, and even afterwards.

7. *Alleged ineffability* means that the experience is felt to be beyond words, non-verbal, impossible to describe, yet most persons who insist on the ineffability do in fact make elaborate attempts to communicate the experience.

8. *Transiency* means that the psychedelic peak does not last in its full intensity, but instead passes into an afterglow and remains as a memory.

9. *Persisting positive changes in attitudes and behavior* are toward self, others, life and the experience itself.

The reasons for the great variety of psychedelic experiences (characterized here under five headings) have provided a fascinating research problem and are now generally recognized to be caused by dosage and the extra-drug variables of set and setting. Of course, most sessions do not contain just one kind of experience. In fact it is not uncommon for all five types to be present in a single psychedelic experience, though in varying proportions.

Dosage appears to be a crucial variable. Each individual has his own range of tolerance and response to any drug, and no absolute figures can be quoted. In the low dose range, for most people, below 200 μg of LSD, the probability is great for the emergence of aesthetic, cognitive and psychodynamic experience. At somewhere between 200 μg and 400 μg of LSD, there appears to be a critical level beyond which psychedelic mystical experience becomes possible, which can be compared to the minimal amount of thrust needed for a rocket to launch itself into orbit. Psychotic experiences are possible at any dosage level, but are much more probable at the higher doses.

The presence of the drug at a certain dosage is a necessary but not sufficient condition, because the extra-drug variables of set and setting play a crucial role in determining the kind of drug response. Psychological set is here defined as factors within the subject, such as personality, life history, expectation, preparation, mood prior to the session and, perhaps most important of all, the ability to trust, to let go, to be open to whatever comes. The setting is here defined as factors outside the individual, such as the physical environment in which the drug is taken, the psychological and emotional atmosphere to which the subject is exposed, how he is treated by those around him and what the experimenter expects the drug reaction to be. A person who has taken a psychedelic drug seems to be much more sensitive to non-verbal cues, perhaps because of an increase in suggestibility, but the exact role of suggestibility is a problem that needs to be further investigated.

It seems clear that the drug is only a trigger, a catalyst or facilitating agent. The kind of psychedelic reaction is largely dependent upon extra-drug variables. Also, at the present state of knowledge, the exact content is impossible to predict with certainty. Psychotic reactions are the easiest to produce; mystical experiences are the hardest, certainly not automatic, even under optimal conditions. Much more needs to be learned.

We turn now to an examination of the evidence that psychedelic mystical experiences actually occur. Most researchers who have worked with LSD in either a therapeutic or a supportive setting have reported the occurrence of mystical experiences in varying degrees of frequency. Some workers, especially most of the European psycholytic therapists, have not been very much interested in such experiences and, in fact, have tried to discourage their occurrence as an unwanted distraction. The frequency with that kind of set and setting is much less, but, even so, these experiences are still reported. As time has gone on, some of the European psychiatrists who have heard about the work done in Canada and the United States have become more interested (Arendsen-Hein, 1967; Johnsen, 1967).

Dr. Arnold Ludwig, of the Mendota State Hospital in Madison, Wisconsin, has purposely programmed his LSD sessions to focus on psychodynamic issues and has definitely not encouraged mystical experiences, as he has informed me personally. Interestingly enough, this kind of experience has occurred anyway in some patients, who then often sought out the hospital chaplain for discussions of religious issues.

Houston and Masters (Masters and Houston, 1966) report a series of 206 subjects with whom they have worked, but of whom little more than 3% were considered to have had true mystical experiences. Such figures need to be interpreted cautiously unless a careful definition with some kind of method for quantifying the experience is established.

A questionnaire has been developed that is based on the nine characteristics of spontaneous mystical experiences outlined above (Pahnke, in unpublished thesis). For any subject the percentage of the maximum possible score for each category can be determined. Varying degrees of completeness are possible, but to be counted as a mystical experience it was decided that both the total score and the score in each separate category must be at least 60% to 70%. This questionnaire has been used in two studies that I have conducted.

The first was carried out on Good Friday in 1962 to test the hypothesis that persons who were given psilocybin would have experiences similar to those reported by spontaneous mystics. Twenty theological students from relatively similar religious and socio-economic backgrounds, after medical and psychiatric screening, were carefully prepared in groups of four with two leaders for each group. All thirty participants listened over loud-speakers to a meditative Good Friday service in a private basement chapel while the actual service was in progress in the church above. The experiment was so designed that half of the subjects received 30 mg of psilocybin and the rest, who became the control group, got as an active placebo 200 mg of nicotinic acid, which causes no psychic effects, only warmth and tingling of the skin. From our preparation all the subjects knew that psilocybin caused autonomic changes. Those who got nicotinic acid thought that they had received psilocybin, and suggestion was thus maximized for the control group. The drugs were administered double-blind, so that neither the experimenter nor the participants knew the specific contents of any capsule. Data were collected by tape recording, written account, the mystical-experience questionnaire and personal interview. When all the data were analyzed, the scores of psilocybin subjects were higher to a statistically significant degree in all categories than those of the control subjects. In regard to degree of completeness, only three or four of the ten psilocybin subjects reached the 60% to 70% level of completeness, whereas none of the control subjects did.

The second series of experiments was performed at the Massachusetts Mental Health Center during 1965 and 1966, an account of which is now being prepared. Forty carefully screened normal volunteers were selected. Most of the subjects were over thirty and held responsible positions in the community as professional people. The sensational publicity about LSD in the popular press added difficulties to our recruitment. We rejected more than 50% of our volunteers on the basis of medical and psychiatric history, physical examination, psychological testing and psychiatric interview. After three hours of preparation, psilocybin was administered to four subjects at a time in a carefully prepared room with cut flowers, pictures of nature scenes, candlelight and a place for each subject to recline and relax. Silence was maintained during a six-hour program of classical music. The setting was supportive, and there were no interruptions for testing during the session. We encouraged the subjects to relax and to let the music carry them. At the present time, the data are not completely analyzed, and all that can be reported are some preliminary impressions. First, the procedure seemed safe for carefully screened normals. No one suffered physical or psychological harm even after a one year follow-up. Second, 20% to 40% of the subjects had a mystical experience, depending on the level of completeness desired. Third, 95% of the subjects said that they would be willing to take the drug again, perhaps sometime in the future, but not too many were eager to do so right away. Having had such powerful experiences, they expressed a desire for time to integrate what had been learned.

In comparison to the 3% of mystical experiences reported by Houston and Masters, and the 20% to 40% in our two studies, some 75% of over 100 patients from the alcoholism project at the Spring Grove State Hospital in Baltimore have had intense mystical experiences during their first session with LSD. It should be remembered that of these patients each had between twelve and twenty hours of individual therapy before his session, which was run individually. In our sessions we had only three hours of preparations, and the sessions were run in groups of four. Individual monitoring seems to help guide someone toward a positive experience. At Spring Grove everything is done to ensure optimal conditions (Kurland, Unger, Shaffer and Savage, 1967).

An important consideration is whether or not such mystical experiences are religious. A simple identification of religious experience with mystical experience fails to take into account the many definitions of religion. Religions vary in their emphasis upon mysticism, although there is a tendency to make the mystical element the most important characteristic of religion, especially among psychologists of religion who have been interested in the dramatic phenomena of the mystical experience. William James reflected this attitude by his preference for religion that is an "acute fever" rather than a "dull habit." Not all religious experience is necessarily mystical in the sense of our definition of mystical experience given below. Pratt, for example, divides religion into four kinds or aspects, of which the mystical is only one, the other three being the traditional, the rational and the practical or moral (Pratt, 1921). Even when quite emotionally meaningful, participation in a particular religion by observing religious laws, through intellectual belief in a certain creed or theology or in institutional membership and attendance at rites and rituals may not result in or be the product of mystical experience.

On the other hand, all mystical experience is not necessarily religious. Again much depends upon how one chooses to define religion. If one makes the concept of a "personal God" central to the definition of religion, many forms of mystical experience could not be considered religious. The phenomena of mystical experience may occur outside the framework of any formal religion with no reference to an articulated theology.

The problem is by-passed or merely indicated, rather than

solved, by broadening the definition of religion to include any experience that would qualify as mystical by our criteria. Tillich, for example, considers an experience religious when it gives ultimate meaning, structure and direction to human experience, or when one is concerned "ultimately" (Tillich, 1951). Better, perhaps, is Huston Smith's definition in an unpublished address. He has defined as a religious experience one that elicits from the experiencer a centered response from the core of his being. Since his being includes feelings, thoughts and will, a religious experience triggers in the experiencer a triple movement—a movement of the emotions in awe, of the mind in belief and of the will in obedience. Here we return to the important ninth characteristic of mystical experience. What changes are there in the person's life? What does he do about it in terms of some religious discipline? If we accept Smith's definition of religious experience and compare it with the nine characteristics, we can perhaps say that such a psychological definition of mystical experience has at least something religious about it. Whether or not mystical experience is religious depends upon one's definition of religion.

Rather than labor the point, the following examples of actual experimental mystical experiences may help the reader to decide whether such experiences would fit his personal definition of religion. The first is the experience of a Christian ministerial student who took a compound from the psilocybin series in a carefully controlled experiment that was conducted in a German research institute under the supervision of an experimenter who was not particularly interested in mystical experiences.

> I hesitate to attempt a summary of my drug experience as I am acutely aware of the inability of linguistic symbols to contain, or even accurately reflect, the dynamics of 'mystic' consciousness. In the words of the Russian poet Tyutchev, I feel as though 'A thought that's spoken is a lie'. To seek to condense any of my experiences into words is to distort them, rendering them finite and impure. In so acknowledging the profound ineffability of my experience, I am not trying to write poetry— although in the final analysis this may well be the only possible means of verbal expression—but intend only to convey the feelings of frustration and futility with which I begin this report.

Now, four days after the experience itself, I continue to feel a deep sense of awe and reverence, being simultaneously intoxicated with an ecstatic joy. This euphoric feeling . . . includes elements of profound peace and steadfastness, surging like a spring from a depth of my being which has rarely, if ever, been tapped prior to the drug experience. The spasmodic nature of my prayer life has ceased, and I have yielded to a need to spend time each day in meditation which, though essentially open and wordless, is impregnated by feelings of thanksgiving and trust. This increased need to be alone is balanced by what I believe to be a greater sensitivity to the authentic problems of others and a corresponding willingness to enter freely into genuine friendships. I possess a renewed and increased sense of personal integration and am more content simply to 'be myself' than previously.

. . . Relatively soon after receiving the drug, I transcended my usual level of consciousness and became aware of fantastic dimensions of being, all of which possessed a profound sense of reality.

. . . It would seem more accurate to say that I existed 'in' these dimensions of being as I had not only transcended my ego, but also the dichotomy between subject and object.

It is meaningful to say that I ceased to exist, becoming immersed in the ground of Being, in Brahman, in God, in 'Nothingness,' in Ultimate Reality or in some similar religious symbol for Oneness. . . .

The feelings I experienced could best be described as cosmic tenderness, infinite love, penetrating peace, eternal blessing and unconditional acceptance on one hand, and on the other, as unspeakable awe, overflowing joy, primeval humility, inexpressible gratitude and boundless devotion. Yet all of these words are hopelessly inadequate and can do little more than meekly point towards the genuine, inexpressible feelings actually experienced.

It is misleading even to use the words 'I experienced,' since during the peak of the experience (which must have lasted at least an hour) there was no duality between myself and what I experienced. Rather, I *was* these feelings, or ceased to be in them and felt no loss at the cessation. This was especially evident when, after having reached the mystic peak, a recording of Bach's 'Fantasia and Fugue in G Minor' was played. At this time it seemed as though I was not M. R. listening to a recording, but paradoxically *was* the music itself. Especially at one climax in the Fantasia, the 'love' I was experiencing became so overwhelming as to become unbearable or even painful. The tears I shed at this moment were in no sense those of fear, but ones of uncontainable joy.

. . . During the height of the experience, I had no consciousness of time or space in the ordinary sense. I felt as though I was beyond seconds, minutes, hours, and also beyond past, present, and future. In religious language, I was in 'eternity.'

. . . let me affirm that even with my acquaintance with mystic literature of both east and west, coupled with the profound appreciation of natural and artistic beauty I have always enjoyed, I know I could never have understood this experience, had I not lived it myself. The dimensions of being I entered surpassed the wildest fantasies of my imagination and, as I have said, leave me with a profound sense of awe. . . . In no sense have I an urge to formulate philosophical or theological dogmas about my experience. Only my silence can retain its purity and genuineness.

It may be objected that a divinity student would obviously have such an experience because of his familiarity with mysticism and religious language. In the Good Friday experiment, however, the control subjects with the same amount of suggestion did *not* have mystical experiences. Also the next several examples were written by chronic, hospitalized alcoholics who had received LSD treatment and who did not have the same interest in religion and mysticism. The accounts are perhaps even more vivid in their simple straightforwardness. Following are excerpts of accounts from four different patients (Unger, 1965).

I found myself drifting into another world and saw that I was at the bottom of a set of stairs. At the very top of these stairs was a gleaming light like a star or jewel of exceptional brilliance. I ascended these stairs and upon reaching the top, I saw a gleaming, blinding light with a brilliance no man has ever known. It had no shape nor form, but I *knew* that I was looking at God himself. The magnificence, splendor, and grandeur of this experience cannot be put into words. Neither can my innermost feelings, but it shall remain in my heart, soul, and mind forever. I never felt so clean inside in all my life. All the trash and garbage seemed to be washed out of my mind. In my heart, my mind, my soul, and my body, it seemed as if I were born all over again.

A feeling of great peace and contentment seemed to flow through my entire body. All sounds ceased and I seemed to be floating in a great, very very still void or hemisphere. It is impossible to describe the overpowering feeling of peace, contentment, and being a part of goodness itself that I felt. I could feel my body dissolving and actually becoming a part of the goodness and peace that was all around me. Words can't describe this. I feel an awe and wonder that such a feeling could have occurred to me.

At the peak or climax of my experience, I realized a great scene was about to unfold within myself. I actually shook and shuddered at what I felt. A tremendous earthquake feeling was building up in me. There was a tremendous force, and I came and saw a glorious beauty of space unfold before me, of light, color, and of song and music, and not only of one thing good and beautiful, but of a oneness in fellowship, a wanting to belong to this greatness of beauty and goodness that unfolded before my eyes, and that I felt.

Suddenly, I could see my family handing me great love. It seemed to be pouring out of their hearts. I cried, not bitter tears, but tears of beauty and joy. A beautiful organ was playing in the background, and it seemed as if angels were singing. All of a sudden I was back in eternity. There was music and beauty. Peace and happiness, tranquillity—could not possibly describe my feelings. My heart was filled with joy that was overwhelming. Just a beauty and peace that I have never known. At this point, I felt that time was thousands of years ago, thousands of years from now, and now.

The profound emotional impact that these experiences have on people can be sensed. The promising possibility that such positive experiences may have therapeutic value is one implication. Another is the usefulness of such a tool for investigating profound mystical experiences that heretofore have been hard to study scientifically because of their rarity.

The basic psychological experience goes beyond any particular framework, but does lend itself to many possible interpretations afterwards, since the rational mind inevitably goes to work and tries to understand. For example, the mystical experience of union or fusion with its concomitant characteristics has been interpreted in many ways: fading or melting into the universal pool, boundless being, the void, *satori, nirvana, samadhi,* the *atman-Brahman* identity; the awareness of a "Beyond," "More" or pure "Self;" or union with God. Yet in spite of the particular interpretation, the psychological experience itself is the basis.

This experience of encounter with what is felt to be a divine dimension deep within a person is not new. It has been reported throughout the centuries in the history of man's spiritual quest. It should be remembered that there are psychotic states of mind in which people also speak in religious metaphors, such as, of meeting God or of being God. The similarities and differences between psychosis and mysticism form an interesting area that needs much more serious study and analysis, for the answers are by no means worked out as yet.

One objection sometimes raised against calling these drug-facilitated experiences mystical or religious is that the accomplishment of something usually considered so rare and unattainable except by extraordinary effort or great merit now seems too easy. What seems like a short-cut causes a feeling of uneasiness. Perhaps the Puritan ethic, so pervasive in our culture, is the psychological explanation. Pleasure is supposed to be earned through hard work and painful struggle.

Indications are, however, that what one *does* with a psychedelic experience may be more important than merely *having* it. Without integration into the on-going life of the individual, the experience may be only an irrelevant memory, no matter how beautiful. Much work is needed to integrate the insights from LSD when used as a part of psychotherapy. The analogy might be drawn of a trip to a new country. If the traveller knew nothing about the history and culture of this country, he might have an interesting trip, but only a fast-fading memory would remain. If, on the other hand, before he departed, he learned as much as possible about the country, its language and customs, talked with people who had been there before him and prepared himself fully, he would probably not only enjoy the experience more, but could utilize it to enrich his life afterwards by thinking, reading and talking about it with others who had made such an experience an integral part of their lives.

At the present time there is a growing ferment of excitement and alarm caused by the religious movement that has been inspired by psychedelic drugs. Already there are four major psychedelic churches, which have been founded by persons who are convinced that their psychedelic experiences have religious implications. These four churches are The League for Spiritual Discovery, The Neo-American Church, The Native American Church and The Church of the Awakening.

The League for Spiritual Discovery, or L.S.D., is the most recent, having been founded by Timothy Leary in September of 1966, and it already claims from three hundred to five hundred members. The psychedelic celebrations that have been performed in some major cities throughout the country have received considerable publicity. These "light shows" have attempted to portray some psychedelic phenomena, but people who have actually had an LSD experience seem to agree that only a crude facsimile is produced. Leary has used these occasions to give psychedelic sermons about his church. The central message has been summarized as "Turn on, tune in and drop out." In essence, the message is of withdrawal, but not from everything, not from all social life, with nothing in its place. The withdrawal is from the meaningless games in which we are involved, to allow full-time committment to spiritual exploration, which Leary feels is the most important reason for living. An attempt is made to criticize modern American culture.

The Neo-American Church was founded in 1964 by a psychologist, Arthur Kleps, who calls himself Chief Boo-Hoo, the Patriarch of the East. Kleps states that the purpose of this title is to remind him not to take himself too seriously. Membership now allegedly numbers over six hundred. LSD is their sacrament, and one of their main beliefs is that alteration of consciousness with LSD is a religious right of any citizen.

The Neo-American Church should not be confused with the Native American Church, which has deep historical roots going back to the religious practices of the Aztecs in Mexico before the time of Christ. When the Spaniards came, they tried to stamp out the use of peyote, but the custom persisted underground. Sometime between 1700 and 1880, the religious use of peyote spread across the Rio Grande River into the southwestern United States and from there to the Plains and then all the way into Canada and as far east as Wisconsin and Michigan. The church has been legally incorporated in Oklahoma since 1918. At present membership has been estimated at anywhere from 50,000 to 250,000 Indians, with only a few white members. Peyote is used in a religious ceremony as their sacrament, which they feel is essential to their church.

Some important features of the ceremony are constant among different groups. The rite is an all-night affair extending from about 8:00 p.m. on Saturday until about 8:00 a.m. on Sunday. It usually takes place around a central fire in a tepee and is led by four or five Indian officials. The ritual begins with prayer, followed by the singing of songs by each participant in turn accompanied by the water drum, ingestion of the sacramental peyote and contemplation. Although the contents of the individual prayers and songs are spontaneous, the ritual as a whole follows a definite pattern. At midnight there is a water-drinking ceremony, and at dawn parched corn in sweetened water, fruit and dried sweetened meat are eaten. [For a detailed description of the ritual with diagrams of the arrangement of participants, see Omar C. Stewart's *Washo-Northern Paiute Peyotism,* Volume XL, Number 3 of the Publications in American Archaeology & Ethnology of the University of California (1944); and compare to Weston La Barre's *The Peyote Cult,* Number 19 of Yale University Publications in Anthropology, an enlarged edition of which was published in 1964 by The Shoe String Press of Hamden, Connecticut.].

Because the ceremony is regarded as very sacred by the Indians, preparation for the rite is taken seriously. Proper preparation includes being physically clean, spiritually pure, psychologically humble and in a mood for concentrated meditation (Slotkin, 1956). The participants feel that peyote aids contemplation by increasing their powers of introspection, sensitizing their consciences and producing visions of great meaning. Throughout the ceremony the participants conduct themselves with due solemnity. White men who have attended these worship services as observers or as participants have taken peyote with the Indians in a receptive manner and have been impressed by the serious and sacred nature of the ceremony (Osmond, 1961; Schultes, 1963; Slotkin, 1961).

The Church of the Awakening was founded in 1958 by two married physicians, John and Louisa Aiken from New Mexico. The church has grown slowly but steadily and has at present about 350 members. Only people who have demonstrated a serious interest in spiritual awakening have been encouraged to join. The members claim that their spiritual lives have been deepened because of participation in psychedelic ceremonies using their sacrament peyote. The use of the sacrament is restricted to once every three months, if even that often. The major emphasis seems to be on integration of spiritual insights into the on-going life of the individual member.

There are certain legal problems posed by the existence of psychedelic churches. Both natural products, like peyote, cactus buttons, mushrooms or morning glory seeds, and synthetic chemicals, like LSD, psilocybin or mescaline, are considered drugs by the law when taken into the human body and thus requiring medical supervision. Because this is the way our society has defined things, there is really no legal mechanism or social sanction for a church to use these substances for spiritual exploration. Unwillingness to accommodate to this fact has caused legal difficulties for Timothy Leary, Arthur Kleps and some of their followers. But the issue becomes clouded because the religious use of peyote in the Native American Church has been permitted by the Food and Drug Administration and by the Supreme Court of California. The matter becomes even more complex when Dr. John Aiken, a licensed physician, seeks to administer peyote for what he considers *bona fide* religious purposes. If he is not allowed to do so, and the Indians are, does this constitute discrimination against white people? Undoubtedly, religious freedom and related issues will receive much publicity in the years ahead as test cases reach the courts. If the matter is decided by outlawing all religious use of psychedelic substances, even by the Native American Church, it may turn into another sorry example of the white man's disregarding the sensitivities and cultural heritage of the American Indian.

In the meantime there is an increasing need for organized religion to consider the impact of the psychedelic religious movement. If instead of the collapse of a fad, as some predict, there is continued interest, growth and enthusiasm, what might be the effect on religion in America? Persons having had powerful psychedelic mystical experiences may well feel that organized religion, in contrast, is moribund and irrelevant to their needs. Such a trend could be perceived as a threat, and the churches might feel a need to encourage suppression of psychedelic drugs. On the other hand, it can be speculated that with an imaginative and creative approach to an increasing amount of mystical experience, revitalization of religious life in the churches could occur. The churches could help people to integrate such profound experiences with the aid of meaningful and appropriate religious symbols. Such people do tend to talk about their drug experiences in religious terms. In our experimental work with divinity students and ministers, those who had a meaningful religious framework were much helped in using positive psychedelic experiences to understand their faith more existentially.

Some definite dangers, however, are posed by the growing use, religious and otherwise, of psychedelic drugs. The possible dangers to the individual have been fully discussed at this conference. It should be emphasized that unsupervised and unskilled use will inevitably lead to psychiatric casualties in a certain, as yet unknown, percentage of cases. The most obvious reasons are lack of screening, inadequate preparation, unskilled handling during the drug reaction, and little or no help with useful integration after the experience. The dangers to society have also been mentioned. If more and more people drop out and withdraw, can society continue to function?

If psychedelic drugs really can change people's goals, values, motivations and needs for achievement, the impact could be considerable on our society, in which there is so much stress on money, power and status. Less emphasis on these traditional goals, coupled with the availability of more leisure time, could alter our style of life. Some argue that such changes in moderation might be healthy, yet it is possible that widespread adoption of a radical change in outlook might be disastrous to a society that wants mainly to multiply its Gross National Product and to compete successfully. Such issues need realistic and sensitive consideration.

There has been too much heat and perhaps not enough light propagated by the psychedelic drugs. Because of mass-media coverage, certainly everyone today has heard of LSD. Interestingly enough, almost everyone has a definite opinion, no matter how little or how much he knows about the field. These opinions, pro or con, usually have a deep emotional basis. Certainly the reason is more than just an abhorrence of drug taking, because other drugs such as tranquilizers, sleeping pills and alcohol are taken freely with no such emotional reaction. The dangers of negative consequences such as psychological breakdown appear to be a logical reason, but since most drug experiences are positive, there must be an additional explanation. A deeper reason may lie in the nature of the profound emotional experiences, often considered religious, which seem to have the power to change a person's values and to generate enthusiasm and inspiration in a direction perhaps not shared by society in general. Such consequences may be seen as a threat when considered logically, but felt even more powerfully to be so at a subliminal or non-rational level.

Our society is faced with the fact that the use of psychedelic drugs is spreading rapidly. Do we have the capacity and wisdom to deal constructively with this problem, or will we seek a solution by restrictive legislation and police force? In this instance, suppression has much less a chance of succeeding than in the illegal use of narcotics, which has not been stopped. Throughout history when enough people have really wanted something, no restrictive measures have worked. Laws did not stop the introduction of coffee into Europe, nor the consumption of alcohol in the United States during Prohibition.

What will undoubtedly result, however, from a rigid suppression of psychedelic drugs is a severe inhibition of research in this area. The more laws that are passed, the more the public identifies the drugs with something negative. People in power, in both the public and academic realms, are influenced by public reaction and the mass media, and when research is proposed, there is hesitation and lack of support. The decline of research with psychedelic drugs has already occurred. Dr. Harold Abramson, one of the early pioneers in LSD research, has commented that an interested layman can use LSD more easily in our society today than can a doctor who wants to do legitimate research. The joint committee now set up by the N.I.M.H. and the F.D.A. to screen proposals will possibly enable more research to begin in the near future.

Research is especially important in regard to the individual and the societal problems caused by the growing use of psychedelic drugs. Education rather than suppression would seem a more effective solution, and more research is needed to learn the unknown facts about many aspects of these drugs. We need more knowledge about their biological and psychological mechanisms of action, their therapeutic possibilities, dangers and long-term effects. Valid statistics about chance of harm would be useful in calculating a realistic pleasure-to-risk ratio.

An important area for more research is the effect of psychedelic drugs on relatively stable, well-adjusted persons. Many of the people who have taken LSD and upon whom some of the conclusions abouts its dangers are based were already drop-outs before encountering the drug. For purposes of education and guidance it is important that we base our facts on drug effects in normals rather than on retrospective analysis of drop-outs. No one knows how many successful people who did *not* drop out or withdraw from their place in society have found that psychedelic experience can be an enriching part of their total lives, without eclipsing other interests and responsibilities.

There are many questions that can only be answered by careful and well controlled research. For example, what are the exact conditions responsible for the production of aesthetic, cognitive or mystical experiences? All the extra-drug variables of set and setting need to be studied intensively. An interesting project would be to follow a group of persons who would have LSD sessions at regular intervals for three to five years, or to do a longitudinal study on a group of persons who had only a few sessions and then were followed over a period of time. In a small group who might take LSD together, other phenomena such as the effect on group discussion, group interaction and group cohesion could be measured.

The sociology of religion has an extraordinary opportunity for research in the psychedelic religious movement. Here is a chance to study the formation and growth of what may become an important form of religion in the United States. The small cult-like groups, the evangelistic ferment, the utopian ideals, the struggle for survival—all these elements can be studied for better understanding of what has gone on when other religious movements emerged in the past. Dr. R. Blum (Blum *et al.,* 1964) has made a start in this area, but other points of view would also be helpful. Participant-observers, who would be more in rapport with those in the movement, might add valuable additional data to the field.

With regard to the future, psychedelic drugs seem to be here to stay as a fact of our present existence. The experiences are much too powerful and have too many implications to be dismissed as a passing fad. Indications are that the use will increase rather than decrease and may have more influence on American life than we now imagine. Certainly researchers with LSD even ten years ago would not have predicted what has happened. More surprises may be in store for us. Work needs to be done with these drugs without delay in a disciplined scientific way rather than permitting a black-market underground to undertake experiments by default.

If these drugs are ever going to be used legitimately, training centers will have to be established, because specialized training under supervision is needed to insure maximal safety. The work thus far at the Spring Grove State Hospital has indicated that even very unstable people can be treated with LSD in relative safety if specific procedures are employed. These centers can be used for the training not only of psychiatrists, but also of psychologists, social workers, ministers or any one else who might have a role in treatment with these drugs. Some day it may even be possible to establish places where interested, serious people could go to take LSD in maximal safety under the supervision of trained personnel. Such a suggestion is utopian at present and may take a long time in being developed, but it is possible in the future.

Some people, however, and especially students, are not content to wait and are asking themselves the existential question "Should I take LSD now, on my own?" It is obvious that anyone who really wants to obtain the drug and take it can do so. No amount of admonition to the contrary from college administrators can really stop anyone. It remains a personal decision, but anyone contemplating such a course of action would be wise to consider some basic facts.

First, there is a definite risk, which is certainly greater in un-controlled than in controlled conditions. The work at Spring Grove and elsewhere has demonstrated that with skilled handling the risk is minimal. Psychedelic drugs are like other powerful tools in that the risk is greatly dependent upon the way they are used. For example, for eye surgery a skilled surgeon is needed, not a watchmaker, no matter how skilled he might be in the use of fine instruments. The use of psychedelic drugs also requires specialized training for maximal safety. At the Spring Grove Hospital, three to six months, or longer, are needed to train a therapist. The fact that safe procedures have been worked out, however, is not much help at present to someone who would like to take a psychedelic drug under supervision, because at present no authorized research in the United States is being done with normal persons.

Another thing to consider is the time of life. Many persons in college are going through an identity crisis and are trying to decide where they are really going with their lives. Because a psychedelic drug experience may affect judgement, it is probably not a good idea to make a major life decision within three months after a drug session. People undergoing intensive psychotherapy or psychoanalysis are given the same advice. Decisions made at such a time may turn out to be regretted later, especially when no guidance is available during and after the drug session. People who have a psychedelic experience when they are older and have successfully settled some of the crucial issues of their lives probably have a better chance for an enriching experience. It would seem that the more life experience a person has had, the better, just as the program fed to a computer is the basis upon which the results are produced.

It is a misconception to imagine that LSD is the magic answer to anything. Hard work is needed to utilize the experience, and follow-up therapy with the therapist who guided the drug session can be very helpful. Persons who take a psychedelic drug to "work out their own problems" not only may be disappointed but also may unearth additional conflicts. More than a few people have been unpleasantly surprised by what emerged with great force from the unconscious.

In spite of the very real dangers in self-experimentation, anyone with a serious and scientific interest in this fascinating area of research would not be discouraged about the prospects of legitimate research. There is much work to be done, and people of the highest caliber will be needed in the near future if we are to gain new knowledge about these drugs and their possible applications. Ideally, an interdisciplinary approach should be used involving the joint efforts of psychiatrists, psychologists, social workers, clergymen, theologians and philosophers.

Anyone interested in this field should get the best possible training in the discipline of his choice. It has been said: "Turn on, tune in and drop out." This can be paraphrased a bit as follows: Turn on your motivation in the most concentrated way possible; tune in to everything that's relevant to equip yourself in the way of training for the work you want to do in the field; and then, instead of dropping out, you will be ready to drop into a worthwhile and interesting career, one that may be full of great satisfactions and a sense of accomplishment, because this is an exciting area.

A striking example of a future psychedelic research possibility is the work with terminal-cancer patients. This area is relevant to a discussion of religion and LSD, because the experience of death has a crucial place in almost all religions. In spite of much talk and concern, and perhaps guilt about the way terminal patients are treated, not much has really changed in this anxiety-ridden situation in our culture. Many times there is a growing isolation from meaningful interpersonal involvement, as all efforts are bent toward making the patient "comfortable."

Psychedelic therapy may have a role to play to make life more livable for terminal patients. LSD was first tried for its analgesic effect, which was found to be considerable (Blum *et al.,* 1964; Kast, 1963; Kast, 1964*a*; Kast, 1964*b*). More important, perhaps, was the finding that fear, anxiety and apprehension were lessened in some cases (Kast, 1966). By working with patients and their families, the opportunity for an increase in interpersonal closeness was afforded, especially in the wake of a powerful psychedelic experience (Cohen, 1965). Current research to explore these initial leads is only in the pilot stage, but it appears to be a promising approach to help ease the agony and isolation of death, both for those who will be left behind and for the one who must face the end of his life.

In conclusion, let us ponder the wide influence that the accidental discovery of LSD in a Swiss pharmaceutical laboratory has exercised throughout the world. There have been far-reaching effects in all kinds of research, especially in biochemistry, pharmacology, psychiatry, psychology, sociology, philosophy and religion. The interdisciplinary implications seem broad indeed. In spite of the dangers that are certainly potential in the use of this powerful tool, it has always been man's destiny to push ahead in order to increase his knowledge. This area is no exception, but those who undertake such research bear a heavy responsibility.

REFERENCES

Abramson, H. A. (ed.) *The Use of LSD in Psychotherapy and Alcoholism.* Indianapolis: Bobbs-Merrill, 1967.

Arendsen-Hein, G. W. Dimensions in psychotherapy. In H. A. Abramson (ed.), *The Use of LSD in Psychotherapy and Alcoholism.* Indianapolis: Bobbs-Merrill, 1967.

Blum, R., *et al. Utopiates: The Use and Users of LSD–25.* New York: Atherton Press, 1964.

Cohen, S. LSD and the anguish of dying. *Harper's,* August, 1965.

Harman, W. W., McKim, R. H., Mogar, R. E., Fadiman, J., and Stolaroff, M. J. Psychedelic agents in creative problem-solving: a pilot study. *Psychol. Repts* (Monogr. Suppl.), 1966, *2–V19*: 211.

Johnsen, G. Indications for psycholytic treatment with different types of patients. In H. A. Abramson (ed.), *The Use of LSD in Psychotherapy and Alcoholism.* Indianapolis: Bobbs-Merrill, 1967.

Kast, E. C. The analgesic action of lysergic acid compared with dihydromorphinone and meperidine. *Bull. Drug Addiction and Narcotics,* 1963, *appendix 27*:3517.

Kast, E. C. LSD and the dying patient. *Chic. Med. Sch. Qu.,* 1966, *26/2*:80.

Kast, E. C. Pain and LSD-25: a theory of attenuation of anticipation. In D. Solomon (ed.), *LSD: The Consciousness-Expanding Drug.* New York: Putnam's, 1964.

Kast, E. C. A study of lysergic acid diethylamide as an analgesic agent. *Anesthesia and Analgesia,* 1964, *43*:285.

Kurland, A. A., Unger, S. M., Shaffer, J. W., and Savage, C. Psychedelic therapy utilizing LSD in the treatment of the alcoholic patient: a preliminary report. *Amer. J. Psychiat.,* 1967, *123/10*: 1202.

Kurland, A. A., Unger, S. M., Savage, C., and Pahnke, W. N. Psychedelic therapy (utilizing LSD) with terminal cancer patients. Presented to the A. P. A. meetings in Detroit on 11 May 1967: to be published.

Masters, R. E., and Houston, J. *The Varieties of Psychedelic Experience.* New York: Holt, Rinehart, 1966.

Osmond, H. Peyote night. *Tomorrow Magazine,* 1961, *9/2*:112.

Osmond, H. A review of the effects of psychotomimetic agents. *Ann. N. Y. Acad. Sci.*, 1957, *66*:429. Reprinted in D. Solomon (ed.), *LSD: The Consciousness-Expanding Drug.* New York: Putnam's, 1964.

Pahnke, W. N. *Drugs and Mysticism: An Analysis of the Relationship between Psychedelic Drugs and the Mystical Consciousness.* Unpublished doctoral thesis submitted to Harvard University in 1963.

Pahnke, W. N., and Richards, W. A. Implications of LSD and experimental mysticism. *J. Relig. Health,* 1966, *5/3*:175.

Pratt, J. B. *The Religious Consciousness: A Psychological Study.* New York: Macmillan, 1921.

Schultes, R. E. Botanical sources of the new world narcotics. *Psychedelic Rev.,* 1963, *1/2*:157. Reprinted in G. Weil *et al.* (eds.), *The Psychedelic Reader.* New Hyde Park, New York: University Books, 1965.

Slotkin, J. S. The peyote way. *Tomorrow Magazine,* 1956, *4/3*:67.

Slotkin, J. S. Menomini peyotism. In D. Ebin (ed.), *The Drug Experience.* New York: Orion Press, 1961.

Tillich, P. *Systematic Theology* (Volume I). Chicago: University of Chicago Press, 1951.

Unger, S. M. The current scientific status of psychedelic drug research. Unpublished paper read to the Conference on Method in Philosophy and the Sciences in New York City on 3 May 1964.

Unger, S. M. The current status of psychotherapeutically-oriented LSD research in the United States. Unpublished paper read to the New York State Psychological Association on 30 April 1965.

6 Governmental and Regulatory Problems with LSD

By MILTON H. JOFFE

CONGRESS has found that the widespread traffic in depressant and stimulant drugs not used under the supervision of licensed practitioners is a threat to the public health and safety and passed a federal law covering both local and interstate traffic in these drugs. Congress again found, as a result of lengthy hearings, that counterfeit drugs represent a fraud at best and are a distinct danger to health when the counterfeit has neither the potency nor the purity of the original and is produced in surroundings and under conditions that do not conform to good manufacturing practices. Counterfeit drugs are the illicitly manufactured or imported drugs that are the source of much of the illicit trade. That a patient's life may depend on drugs having little resemblance to what is prescribed, except in color, size and shape, is a serious matter. The fact that significant connections exist between the counterfeit drug racket and the illegal traffic in amphetamines and barbiturates is not fortuitous, and because of this control of abused drugs and the prosecution of those in the counterfeit business should be tied together in the same law.

This act, once known as *HR-2,* which appeared for presidential signature as *P.L. 89-74,* is the Drug Abuse Control Amendment of 1965, or D.A.C.A. for short. It provided for a seven-month interval between enactment and the effective date of control of the depressant and stimulant drugs. The Bureau of Drug Abuse Control was established early in March of 1966 to enforce this act.

Since this paper concerns both the governmental and the regulatory problems associated with LSD, which is the most notorious, if not the most seriously abused drug, subject to these amendments, I should like to discuss the governmental problem as distinct from the regulatory problem, for reasons that I shall come to after I have elaborated on the regulatory problem by defining what we control, how, where, whom and why.

The *why* of the situation is manifold. There are dangers both to the individual's health and to the public welfare through uncontrolled use of drugs that abolish reality; and there are dangers in the use of drugs whose toxicology, pharmacology, biochemistry and behavioral effects have been insufficiently investigated. Further, the social outlook and the psychological state of the drug takers are certainly not conducive to the continuance or the improvement of an orderly and productive society. It is for these reasons that a law was passed.

The *where* is wherever the problem exists—in the schools and colleges, on the streets, in the home, wherever an individual can manage to go. In terms of our regulatory authorities, the limits are rather less widespread. The Bureau maintains nine field offices, which are located in Boston, New York City, Baltimore, Atlanta, Dallas, Kansas City, Los Angeles, Denver and Chicago, with the New York office having responsibility for Puerto Rico and the Los Angeles office for Hawaii. The *how* of the field agents' work is by virtue of their training and experience as criminal investigators, often as former agents of the Federal Bureau of Investigation or of the Food and Drug Administration, complemented by training in the specifics of drug control. This complementary training in the sociological aspects of the situation, in the psychology of the typical user, in the pharmacology of the drugs and in the legal aspects of their work enables them as well to be public speakers and educators before non-technical but concerned groups, such as P.T.A.'s, Boy Scouts and childrens' welfare groups of all sorts. It is this educational aspect of the work that is more important in the long run than simple enforcement; for if educational work is not done, the enforcement problem will simply grow to unmanageable proportions, and the drug abuse problem cannot be solved.

The *what* do we control is spelled out by the act itself and by supplementary regulations. These distinguish between those drugs that have a legitimate and approved use in the practice of medicine and those whose therapeutic use has not yet been demonstrated, but whose effects and potency are quite evident, the best known of this second class being LSD. You will notice that I group "legitimate and approved" together, for I am not prepared to argue legitimacy of therapeutic use, but the fact is that present approval for practitioner use does not exist for LSD or other hallucinogens.

Among the controlled drugs are amphetamines, barbiturates and others designated by regulation as having a potential for abuse because of their depressant, stimulant or hallucinogenic effect on the central nervous system. They represent a group separate from prescription drugs, although they lie within this category. The control of these drugs rests in the required inventory and records kept by the manufacturers, wholesalers and retailers. D.A.C.A. also provides that no prescription of controlled drugs may be refilled more than five times and becomes void after six months, though it may be renewed by the practitioner if he so desires. The law specifically exempts laboratories engaged in chemical analyses and research or educational institutions from the requirements for registration with the F.D.A., but it does require that they maintain records of receipt and disbursement of these drugs. In addition, possession of such drugs for an individual's personal use or that of his family and their animals is also exempt. In other words, anyone with a legitimate need for such drugs can obtain them, since a physician may prescribe them, and research workers may use them in the course of their investigations.

The hallucinogenic drugs are somewhat different. There is as yet no approved therapeutic use for the hallucinogens, and they cannot be prescribed by a physician. The regulations require that use of the hallucinogens—LSD, DMT, peyote, psilocin and psilocybin—*in vitro or in vivo* be subject to prior approval by the commissioner of the F.D.A. Possession of these drugs for experimental use is not contrary to federal law, but unlicensed manufacturing and giving or selling of these drugs to others, especially to minors, is illegal. The investigational use of these drugs is authorized; present regulations involve coördination between the F.D.A. and the National Institute of Mental Health. A joint committee of nongovernmental experts determines the validity of the proposals, with executive secretaries from F.D.A. and N.I.M.H. committees helping to increase efficiency.

The problem of regulatory control is not unusual in that supervision of the manufacturing and vending of the controlled drugs is no different from supervision of the same factors when only public welfare is in mind.

The immediate question with respect to drug abuse is that of the size of the problem, for the Bureau of Drug Abuse Control has responsibility for drugs other than LSD. No truly meaningful figures exist yet with respect to LSD usage. That use of it is widespread on college campuses is not in doubt. Of 1.5 million college students, perhaps 10% have tried the drug either as occasional or one-time users. Part of the problem lies in determining whether the one-time user becomes an occasional user and the occasional user becomes a consistent user.

Our plans call for a survey of representative populations of various localities in the country. The concentration of drug abusers is not known, but it is expected that 50% of non-narcotic drug abusers are not in New York City, as is probably the case with users of heroin. The mass media have done too good a job dramatizing and glamorizing certain aspects of drug-taking among that portion of the population that is literate, intelligent, curious, young and anxious to be *avant-garde*. It is this group that is probably the most homogenous of any to be found in American society today, held together by a desire to be non-conforming, an attitude now prevalent in colleges, universities and high schools across the entire country.

The group motivations for iconoclastic behavior and the non-conformist attitudes of the individual within the group certainly play a large role in the use of drugs by those whose knowledge of pharmacology and psychology does not reach the level of their certitude regarding the errors of their elders. The rude facts are that toxicology does not admit many errors, that the court of physiological adaptation assesses the severest penalties when its compensatory limits are exceeded, and that the wonderfully adaptive mechanisms of the brain can be pushed beyond reversibility. Even as the major problem of Theseus was to find a way back from his trip through the Minoan labyrinth, so our major problem is to find a sure way back from psychotomimetic experiences, and to date we have neither Ariadne nor Rand-McNally. In addition to the hazard of each trip there is the danger of compounding the risk by multiple excursions into this unknown territory. No one can presently predict the eventual result of a single dose of a psychotomimetic compound, nor can the results of continued use even be estimated. It does appear now that if damage to the central nervous system occurs, whether physiological or behavioral, it cannot be rectified. According to Dr. Louria, the only question at this time is whether permanent damage can result from a single exposure to LSD. It therefore becomes a matter of public concern that there is protection of the individual against his own rash acts, like restrictions on addicting drugs, traffic-safety laws, regulations requiring safety features on automobiles and standards of quality for food and drink.

The resources of the Bureau of Drug Abuse Control consist (as of March of 1967) of about two hundred agents distributed among the field offices, whose mission is criminal investigation of the illegal producers to reduce the supply and to apprehend the purveyors of drugs named in the law. In addition to these agents, there is the Division of Drug Studies and Statistics, which is empowered to do research in certain problem areas—psychological, sociological, pharmacological and non-punitive measures of control. Both field agents and research and headquarters personnel engage in educational activities to the greatest extent possible, which fact leads to the problem that I have termed governmental responsibility rather than regulatory.

This distinction in functions is perhaps artificial, but I want to emphasize the appropriateness of our research and educational efforts as governmental responsibilities other than simple enforcement.

The law states that as evidence accumulates to support findings of drug abuse, the commissioner of the F.D.A. shall have authority, upon the recommendation of expert advice, to place other drugs under the controls previously cited. The problem is twofold: how to determine that such evidence exists and is scientific rather than emotional, is meaningful rather than based on insufficient hard data (and who decides "insufficiency"?); and how to prevent drugs with a high potential for abuse from getting into the market place without stringent control.

There are, of course, several ways in which such evidence may be gathered:

1. Let usage increase without controls until it becomes evident that we have a problem on our hands.
2. Tell the manufacturer to provide evidence that the compound does not have abuse potential and that it causes neither physical nor psychological dependence.

3. Attempt by means of animal experimentation to amass evidence and make the determination on as rational and cautious a basis as is possible.

The fault with the first approach is that we do not escape from an avoidable problem; it is the common fault of always being behind the problem rather than ahead of it. The first alternative leaves the manufacturer to ask the legitimate question "Can you give us the methodology for making the determinations?" The techniques at present do leave much to be desired.

The second alternative, of a scientific approach to the evidence by animal experimentation for which the methodology does not exist, would seem a legitimate governmental function. To supply standards so that industry can conform to government's demands is only reasonable, and this we are now attempting to do. By use of such techniques we shall be able to predict which drugs have the highest abuse potential and thus might present problems.

The providing of standards also leads to a governmental responsibility to give law-enforcement agencies techniques for the identification of controlled drugs, both as chemical compounds *per se* and as compounds circulating in the body after use, and of their metabolites. It also means the identification of counterfeit materials from the standpoint of maintaining purity of the product and preventing economic fraud. It also means supporting research investigations that are aimed at providing information on the drugs themselves and on the drug user and developing techniques to allow the problem to be solved, not just handled.

One of the principal functions of the Bureau of Drug Abuse Control is educational, and to this end the field agents talk to many diverse groups, as I have pointed out. The headquarters staff and the bureau director are much involved in presentations to professional and scientific groups, and the function of the Division of Drug Studies and Statistics is research—psychological, sociological, pharmacological and statistical. We believe that the government is justified in its research into activities that it attempts to control, for the cultural history of man amply demonstrates that punitive measures alone are not a solution to cultural and social problems and that unbiased experimentation leads to more valid results than subjective appraisals. With valid, reproducible scientific data we may be able to suggest modifications of environmental conditions, psychological and educational presentations and the drugs themselves that will reduce the problems of psychological dependence to a minimum. In the situation of drug abuse we believe that the greatest problem facing the government is doing something toward preventing it.

7   Social and Legal Aspects of LSD Usage

By NEIL L. CHAYET

THE law has had a difficult time in dealing with LSD. Because it is an immensely powerful and poorly understood drug, which on the one hand shows great therapeutic promise, but on the other possesses the power to precipitate or to aggravate serious mental disease; because young people and their leaders extol its potential to heighten awareness; because it promises to intensify life by annihilating the tension and boredom of everyday existence; because researchers call for a measure of freedom in trying to discover the potential of LSD; because physicians must treat those who are seriously injured by uncontrolled use of these drugs; because educators must face the tragedies that may befall those within their charge who wish to experiment with the hallucinogens; and finally because of the religious question, LSD poses innumerable problems for our legal system. The law has not yet met this challenge.

Despite the many voices that claim that the law has no right to tell people what they can and cannot do with their own bodies and their own minds, it is clear that some form of regulation is necessary. Dr. Louria has provided us with evidence that clearly supports the need for some sort of regulation.[1] His research has revealed over one hundred patients who have been hospitalized over the past eighteen months with LSD-induced acute psychoses or with chronic schizophrenia or schizoid personality aggravated by the ingestion of LSD. Of this number, 13.1% suffered from what he terms "profound terror," 12.3% exhibited uncontrolled violence, and 8.6% attempted either homicide or suicide. There have even been reports that LSD may cause genetic defects. An article in a recent issue of *Science* (6 March 1967), a weekly journal of the American Association for the Advancement of Science, relates that geneticist Maimon J. Cohen and his colleagues have found chromosomal damage in a preliminary study of a small number of persons who had used LSD.

The youthfulness of those to whom the drug appeals, together with the seriousness of the effects, plainly requires some sort of legislative control. It is equally clear that much of the legislation and regulation attempting to deal with the problem has been spawned in panic with little thought and a lack of understanding of the motivation and complexity of the problem, resulting in either legislative overkill, complete ineffectiveness or both.

In surveying state and federal action, one sees a legislative spectrum running from imposition of the harshest penalties to complete indifference and failure to enact any legislation at all. The majority of states approach the legislative control of all drugs in a uniform manner, totally ignoring varying physiological and psychological effects on the body. To trace the development of this trend, it is necessary to go back to 1932, when the Uniform Narcotic Drug Act (U.N.D.A.) was passed to provide uniform coverage and to offer each state a comprehensive ready-made plan for possible adoption. At that time very few drugs were publicly known or understood in the United States. The U.N.D.A. treated both the opiates and marijuana in the same legislative manner, defining them as "narcotic drugs." All penalties were conceived of in terms of possession, sale, manufacture, use and transfer of a narcotic drug. Using this base, most states continued to expand this comprehensive definition of narcotic drugs as new drugs became misused and as the underground traffic in drugs expanded.

The federal legislation, unlike the state acts based on the uniform law, distinguished between the "hard" drugs (opium, morphine, *etc.*) and the "soft" drugs (marijuana). Many states subsequently followed the lead of the federal government, but only to the extent of this simplistic division of "hard" and "soft" drugs. The states continued to use the "soft" drug classification when the depressant and stimulant drugs as well as the hallucinogens came into popularity. The effect of this was an incongruous jumble of statutory provisions in no way relating punishment to the potentiality for physical harm.

Massachusetts is representative of the jurisdictions that have attempted to deal with LSD through harsh and punitive legislation, the purpose of which seems to make as many felons as possible out of young people who experiment with LSD. The primary means of accomplishing this was to brand LSD a "narcotic" and as such to make it subject to all of the provisions and penalties applying to the true narcotics, such as heroin and opium. The causes of LSD usage have very little to do with those of narcotic usage; the results of LSD usage are very different, yet the Massachusetts legislature has seen fit to treat these two problems in exactly the same way.

An example of the harshness of the Massachusetts legislation is illustrated by the following statute:

> Whoever is present where a narcotic drug is illegally kept or deposited, or whoever is in the company of a person knowing that said person is illegally in possession of a narcotic drug, or whoever conspires with another person to violate the narcotic drugs law, may be arrested without a warrant . . . and may be punished by imprisonment in the state prison for not more than five years.[2]

Thus, the college freshman who attends a party without any knowledge that LSD is in the room is subject to arrest and prosecution for a felony merely by being in the presence of LSD. Party-going can become an extremely hazardous pastime with such legislation on the books.

Another Massachusetts law provides that if a person induces or attempts to induce another person to use unlawfully or to administer a narcotic drug, he is subject to a sentence of ten to twenty years in the state prison for the first offense and of twenty to fifty years for the second offense.[3]

Thus, the student who attempts to have his girl friend accompany him on a "trip" should contemplate the rather lengthy prison sentence that could result. Other provisions of Massachusetts law make it a felony to possess LSD, psilocybin or DMT.[4]

Massachusetts has even done as much as possible to discourage persons who feel that they are addicted or in danger of becoming addicted to a drug from seeking medical assistance. Another provision of Massachusetts law provides that:

Every physician and every hospital treating persons suffering from the chronic use of narcotic drugs shall within seventy-two hours of the first treatment furnish the department of public health with a statement in duplicate containing the name, address, height, weight, date of birth, color of eyes, color of hair, date treated and the name of the narcotic drug the patient used or suffered from. Such information shall be made available for the use of any agency of the common-wealth or the United States which may require it.[5]

The physician who does not comply with this mandate is subject to a fine of up to $2,000 or to imprisonment for up to two years, or to both. In addition to a mandatory breach of the confidentiality inherent in the physician-patient relationship, this law operates to discourage anyone in need of treatment from seeking it, since under this statute the state and local police have complete access to the reported information.

All is not completely black in Massachusetts as far as legislation is concerned. Section 12 of Chapter 17 does establish a drug rehabilitation board, consisting of the commissioners of public health, mental health and corrections. This law calls for the establishment of centers designed to care for persons who are so dependent on narcotic drugs (LSD, DMT and psilocybin included) that they lose their powers of self-control and are thereby a danger to themselves and to the public.

A significant provision of the law is that it applies to those who are arrested on criminal charges, either those enumerated above referring specifically to drug use or any other criminal charge. If a person charged with a crime, theoretically even with first-degree murder, shows symptoms of being a drug addict in accordance with the definition above, he may, at the discretion of the court, be sent to the treatment center in lieu of sentence for a maximal period of three years for treatment. There has been an almost complete failure of implementation in that only one ten-bed center has been established under this act. There is presently a lengthy waiting list, and very little of the potential of this law has been realized. Nevertheless, this legislation is indicative of a more fruitful direction for drug legislation. The young person who has fallen into difficulty with LSD or any drug is much more in need of medical and psychiatric assistance than he is of a lengthy prison term or a large fine.

As a brief aside, the Massachusetts legislature has just passed a law requiring anyone who purchases glue to give his name and address to the vendor. Apparently aimed at diminishing the incidence of glue-sniffing, this law has the somewhat questionable effect of requiring every six-year-old who goes to the five-and-ten-cent store for a bottle of airplane glue to be in full command of his name and address and able to write them. No mention is made in the legislation of what is to be done with all these names and addresses, and the effect of the law upon the incidence of glue-sniffing will be anxiously awaited by all concerned.

New Hampshire has modelled its recently enacted legislation on that of Massachusetts even to the point of incorporating the Massachusetts provision making presence where LSD is kept a crime. The one concession to realistic legislation is that the New Hampshire provision requires a knowledge that the drug is present. The New Hampshire law contains a catch-all provision allowing for the inclusion of "any drug which contains any quantity of a substance which after investigation has been found to have and by regulation of the division of public health services designated as having a potential for its hallucinogenic effect."[6] This would include the recently emergent STP and other substances that are sure to come along in the future. The chart at the end of this paper indicates that thirty-eight states have no legislation specifically relating to LSD.

Connecticut has perhaps the most comprehensive and forward-looking legislation dealing with LSD. This omnibus act, which takes effect on October 1, 1967, covers both marijuana and LSD, but quite explicitly separates the two according to their respective effects on the mind and body and provides different and appropriate penalties. Until July of 1967 Connecticut enjoyed the unusual status of placing LSD in the same category with kosher meat, athletics, consumer brands and weights and measures. This resulted in a rather incompatible combination of responsibilities for the inspectors of the Division of Consumer Protection.

Section one of the new law separately defines amphetamines, barbiturates, cannabis, cocaine and the hallucinogens. There are also two separate categories, the "controlled drugs" and the "narcotic drugs," which are essentially for use with the common properties of each group of drugs. The hallucinogens, including LSD, are defined as "psychodysleptic drugs which assert a confusional or disorganizing effect upon mental processes of behavior and mimic acute psychotic disturbances."[7]

Possession of LSD is a misdeameanor. For each offense the penalty is up to one year in jail or a fine of $1,000, or both.[8] Manufacturing, dispensing and transporting the drug appropriately carry a much greater penalty.

The focus of the federal law is on the attempt to destroy illegal traffic at its source, rather than on imposition of stringent penalties on the user. Only education and medical treatment can eradicate misuse. Connecticut's new statute has these same goals.

There is a penalty for possession, but Connecticut provides specifically for an alternative to a jail sentence, to be found in Section 40(a), which reads:

> If a prosecutor or judge of any court before whom a criminal charge is pending has reason to believe that a person accused of a violation of this act is a drug-dependent person, such prosecutor may apply to the court for appointment of, or the court in its own motion may appoint, one or more physicians to examine the accused person to determine if he is drug dependent. If the accused person is reported to be drug dependent by such physician or physicians, upon agreement between the prosecutor and the accused person, the court may enter an order suspending prosecution for the crime for a period not to exceed one year for a misdemeanor, and two years for a felony and release the accused person to the custody of the commission on adult probation for treatment by the commissioner of mental health. . . . The statute of limitations shall be tolled during the period of suspension.[9]

There are checks on this provision to insure against abuse, but the freedom that the court has to provide for medical treatment instead of jail or fine is the most significant provision of the law.

Ideal legislation would provide for both medical and psychiatric treatment to cope with the dependency factor and the mental disorder that can be caused by use of LSD. Connecticut has both. There are in-patient treatment facilities established under the governance of the Commissioner of Mental Health to "receive and cause medical care and treatment to be administered to any person who believes himself to be a drug-dependent person."[10] Section 50 provides for voluntary admission, but there is also, in section 51, a provision for committment by the court to the in-patient treatment centers for a period not exceeding twenty-four months. Because LSD can cause serious psychiatric problems, the treatment centers are placed under the Department of Mental Health rather than under the Department of Public Health so that the total needs of the LSD patient can be met.

Research has shown that symptoms induced by LSD can recur weeks or even months after ingestion, and emergency psychiatric treatment may well be necessary to deal with a recurring drug-induced psychosis. Connecticut law provides that "[a]ny person who has suddenly become in need of care and treatment in a hospital for mental illness for a psychiatric disorder other than drug dependence, or for drug dependence when his condition is acute and creates a pronounced danger to himself or to the community may be confined in such a hospital, either public or private, under an emergency certificate as hereinafter provided, for not more than thirty days without order of any court. . . ."[11]

As previously mentioned, medical treatment and education should be the primary focus of legislative control of possession and usage of LSD. Regulation of the drug itself should be relegated to the areas of manufacture, distribution and general traffic. Unique to Connecticut's omnibus drug legislation is the following section:

> The effect of alcohol and controlled drugs [including LSD] on health, character, citizenship and personality development shall be taught to pupils above the fifth grade in the public schools. . . . State colleges shall give instruction on the subject prescribed in this section and concerning the best methods for teaching the same.[12]

Other states would do well to follow Connecticut's lead.

The federal law has also achieved a sophisticated approach to the problems of hallucinogens. Section 511 of the Federal Food,

Drug and Cosmetic Act dealing with the depressant and stimulant drugs was amended in 1966 to encompass the hallucinogenic drugs. This act empowers the Commissioner of Food and Drugs to prepare regulations defining the various terms used in the act. One of these, promulgated in January of 1966, is as follows:

> [The term] "depressant or stimulant drug" means any drug which contains any quantity of: . . . (6) any substance which the commissioner [of Food and Drugs], after investigation, has found to have, and by regulation designates as having, a potential for abuse because of its depressant or stimulant effect on the central nervous system or its hallucinogenic effect.[13]

Section 166.3 designates those drugs that the Commissioner has found to have hallucinogenic effect. They are DMT (dimethyltryptamine), LSD-25 or LSD (d-lysergic acid diethylamide), mescaline and its salts, peyote, psilocybin (psilocibin) and psilocy (psilocin).

Although peyote is listed, the following qualifying paragraph is found in section 166.3: "The listing of peyote in this subparagraph does not apply to non-drug use in bona fide religious ceremonies of the Native American Church; however, persons supplying the product to the Church are required to register and maintain appropriate records of receipts and disbursements of the article."

Thus it is clear that LSD is circumscribed by the federal statute; however, the extent of the coverage and prohibitions under the statute are unusual and worthy of comment. Section 511 of the act prohibits manufacturing, compounding or processing of the drug. Exempted from the provisions of the law are registered manufacturers, suppliers, wholesale druggists, pharmacies, practitioners licensed by law to prescribe or administer depressant or stimulant drugs in the course of their professional practice and persons who use depressant or stimulant drugs in research, teaching or chemical analysis. But with LSD there is presently no legitimate manufacturing of the drug since Sandoz Pharmaceuticals, the sole legitimate manufacturer in the United States, ceased manufacture, turning over its total supply to the National Institute of Mental Health.

Section 511 (c) deals with the use and possession of drugs such as LSD and forbids possession except for the personal use of an individual or of a member of such a person's household, or for administration to an animal owned by him or a member of his household. Thus the person who uses LSD or who even wishes to "take a trip" with his dog may not be punished by federal law. The law further provides that in any case when the federal government contends that a person possessed the drug for sale or for a purpose other than his own use, the United States shall have the burden of proving this fact. This makes it very clear that the federal legislation is aimed at the illegal manufacture of the drug and the illegal trafficking in LSD, and not at individual use or possession. Thus a person could probably take LSD in front of a federal agent with legal impunity; and in the many states without legislation dealing with LSD (see chart at the end of this chapter) law-enforcement officials are powerless to deal with the problem once the sale or transfer has been made to the individual user. An appropriate federal official could seize the drug, since the use of the drug would be without a proper prescription and it could not be said to be used in a properly constituted research project. Seizure is possible under federal law, but arrest and punishment are not.

The philosophy behind the federal legislation is an excellent one. It does not seek to make felons of the occasional or even the chronic user, but rather places its emphasis on illegal manufacture and illicit sale of the drug. The result of a complete absence of punishment for personal use and possession does, however, lead to some unfortunate results. In states such as Massachusetts the federal authorities make it a practice to coöperate with the state authorities in making raids and arrests, and the harsh state legislation is almost always utilized with the federal enforcement. It would be far better for the federal legislation to include well-considered provisions regulating use and possession. This would provide a uniform policy of policing LSD throughout the fifty states; it would prevent the invocation of inordinately penalizing state legislation; and in those states without legislation regulating the hallucinogens, it would prevent law enforcement from being completely helpless in controlling illicit possession and use. Legislation controlling possession and use should place a premium on the treatment of those addicted to the drugs or its effects rather than on the infliction of prison terms or fines, as in Connecticut. Use or possession should be deemed a misdemeanor, and minimum fines or sentences should be imposed in appropriate cases; but emphasis should be placed upon psychiatric treatment, combined with probationary periods if necessary. The experience of the Massachusetts Court Clinics has been that the use of the probationary system to enforce psychiatric therapy has been extremely effective.

Penalties for illicit sale or transfer of the drug should remain, but there should be careful differentiation of penalties depending on the age of the person transferring, the age of the person to whom the drug is transferred and the past record of the individual accused.

The federal law, unlike much of the state legislation, does attempt to differentiate the penalty according to realistic guidelines. The illegal sale of LSD is ordinarily punishable by imprisonment for not more than one year or by a fine of not more than $1,000 or by both. A second offense is punishable by imprisonment for not more than three years or by a fine of not more than $10,000 or by both. However, if a person over the age of eighteen sells to a person under twenty-one, he is subject to imprisonment for two years, a fine of $5,000 or both; and for a second offense, to six years and/or a fine of $15,000. As mentioned above, Massachusetts punishes the sale of LSD by a prison term of at least five years and a second offense by at least ten and not more than twenty-five years. Any person who induces another to use unlawfully or to administer a narcotic drug is punished by *not less than ten and not more than twenty-five years,* and for a second offense by not less than twenty and not more than fifty years. There is no differentiation based on the ages of the parties involved.

Yet even with such ominous laws on the books, extensive use of LSD, particularly among the young, continues. It is becoming quite clear that the law alone cannot cope with the problems posed by the illicit use of LSD. The scare technique often operates in a manner that only increases the desire. There is a great deal of litigation presently going on throughout the country involving LSD as well as other drugs, particularly marijuana. Many of the cases are testing the constitutionality of the legislation regulating these drugs. One of the most vociferous opponents of the present legislative structure is Timothy Leary. Mr. Leary is the primary proponent of the argument that use of marijuana and LSD and other hallucinogens is essential to the pursuit of his religion, presently termed the League for Spiritual Discovery, and that the laws prohibiting the use, possession and free trading of the drug are laws that abridge religious freedom and as such contravene the First Amendment of the United States Constitution. The religious-freedom argument is best expressed in a lengthy and excellent brief prepared by Professor Joel Jay Finer of the University of Texas Law School for Mr. Leary's appeal (still pending) from his conviction in a federal district court for violating the federal tax laws. Points made in this brief, while dealing with the question of marijuana, are equally applicable to the freedom-of-religion argument raised on behalf of LSD. The Texas case arose in 1965 when Mr. Leary, accompanied by his daughter and three other passengers, crossed the International Bridge at Laredo leading from Mexico into the United States. According to the brief, "because the automobile contained considerable baggage (and one of the passengers was bearded), the occupants were ordered out of the car. A preliminary search revealed a marijuana seed . . . ."[14] Mr. Leary was convicted by a jury in federal court of unlawfully and knowingly transporting illegally imported marijuana and of unlawfully and knowingly transporting marijuana, as a transferee without having paid the transfer tax required by law. He was sentenced to the maximal fine and imprisonment under each count (a total of thirty years and a fine of $30,000) and ordered to undergo a psychiatric examination in contemplation of a subsequent reconsideration of the sentence.

Mr. Leary appealed. One of his main arguments was that the First Amendment protected him in his good-faith use of marijuana as an integral part of the exercise of his religion. The First Amendment provided that "Congress shall make no law respecting an establishment of religion or prohibiting the free exercise thereof . . . ." Central to Mr. Leary's contention is the fact that marijuana plays an integral role in the exercise of his religion, that the ingestion of marijuana does not present a grave abuse endangering paramount interests, and that the use of marijuana for religious purposes should be fully protected by the "free exercise" clause of the First Amendment. In the brief filed by Mr. Leary's attorney a comparison of the marijuana case is made with the polygamy cases.[15] Mr. Finer cites these cases as the basis of the proposition that only the gravest abuses justify infringement of religion, especially religious worship. The Supreme Court, however, showed the "deepest abhorrence" toward the practice of polygamy, finding that it undermined the principles of democratic government, "fettered the people in stationary despotism, and amounted to a return to barbarism." The Court treated the Mormons' claims that they practiced polygamy in pursuit of their religious beliefs as a "pretense" and "altogether a sophistical plea."[16] Mr. Finer then goes on to assert that "no such damning condemnations can be applied to the ingestion of alcohol, and that no warrant exists for denying that his religious commitment to marijuana is deeply held and was sincerely claimed under oath at the trial."[17]

There has been a good deal of questioning on the subject of whether the use of LSD can be legally justified on the basis of religious freedom, and it is expected that Mr. Leary will use many of the same arguments advanced in this brief in attempting to gain legal acceptance of LSD usage by his League for Spiritual Discovery. One of the most important differences in the two positions, however, is the fact that there is evidence that LSD can be extremely harmful. The religious argument in support of the legalization of marijuana has made little headway, but a case presently pending in Massachusetts is expected to make real progress in attacking the laws that make use of marijuana a felony. This case is based on the premise that marijuana is certainly no more harmful to the body than is alcohol and therefore should be subject to the same types of regulation. The religious argument is not even going to be raised in the Massachusetts case, and it is doubtful whether the issue of religion is essential in the attack on the marijuana laws, or whether it in fact impedes the attack by affecting people in the manner in which only religious issues can.

The situation as far as LSD is concerned is far different, for here we are dealing with a substance acknowledged to be potentially very dangerous in the hands of an inexperienced user. The fact that there is a recognized danger makes it essential that there be another and compelling countering force if the substance is ever to be legalized for general use. With marijuana the religious argument is now not necessary, in view of the scientific evidence demonstrating the lack of danger; with LSD the religious argument is essential.

Let us look for a moment at the merits of the argument that the law making the use and possession of LSD a crime is a law "prohibiting the free exercise" of a religion.

It might be said that there is a case in point on the subject. This would be the case of *People v. Woody*. In this case, the defendants, a group of Navajo Indians, were convicted of violating section 11500 of the California Health and Safety code, which prohibits the unauthorized possession of peyote. The case was appealed to the California Supreme Court, which reversed the decision of the trial court and held that since the defendant Indians used the peyote in a *"bona fide* pursuit of a religious faith, and since the practice does not frustrate a compelling interest of the state, the application of the statute improperly defeated the immunity of the First Amendment of the Constitution of the United States."[18]

Again we see the statement in the court's opinion that "the state may abridge religious practices only upon a demonstration that some compelling state interest outweighs the defendants' interests in religious freedom." The court was troubled by the fact that peyote was a hallucinogenic drug, the effects of which may be extremely serious. The court further stated: "Peyote's principal constituent is mescaline. When taken internally by chewing the buttons or drinking a derivative tea, peyote produces several types of hallucinations, depending primarily upon the user. In most subjects it causes extraordinary vision, marked by bright and kaleidoscopic colors, geometric patterns, or scenes involving humans or animals. In others, it engenders hallucinatory symptoms similar to those produced in cases of schizophrenia, dementia praecox or paranoia. Beyond its hallucinatory effect, peyote renders for most users a heightened sense of comprehension; it fosters a feeling of friendliness toward other persons."[19]

The court went to great lengths to explain the history of peyote and its meaning to the Native American Church, an Indian religious organization with a membership ranging in estimates from 30,000 to 250,000. The court also carefully detailed the procedure scrupulously adhered to by the Indians in the administration and use of the drug. It explained that the "meeting," a ceremony marked by the sacramental use of peyote, "composes the cornerstone of the peyote religion." The meeting convenes in an enclosure and is held from sundown on Saturday to sunrise on Sunday. The first order of business at the meeting is to choose a "sponsor," who supplies for those who attend all the peyote necessary for the meeting and provides breakfast the next morning as well. The persons attending the meeting put on their finest clothing, and there is ceremonial singing, praying and playing of the drum, fan, eagle bore, whistle, rattle and prayer cigarette, which are the symbolic emblems of the Native American Church; however, the central event of the meeting and of the Leary religion consists of the use of the drug in sufficient quantity to produce a hallucinogenic effect.

At a fixed stage in the ritual, the members pass around a ceremonial bag of peyote buttons. Each adult may take four, which is the customary number, or fewer if he desires. Later the members may ask for more peyote, and each member may take as many as four additional buttons. By morning the effect of the peyote disappears, and the users suffer no apparent after-effects, departing after a hearty Sunday-morning breakfast.

The court pointed out that "although peyote serves as a sacramental symbol similar to bread and wine in certain churches, it is much more than a sacrament. Peyote constitutes in itself an object of worship; prayers are directed to it much as prayers are devoted to the Holy Ghost."[20] The court also pointed out that the non-religious use of peyote is considered sacrilegious. The court concluded the first part of the opinion with the statement: "To forbid the use of peyote is to remove the theological heart of Peyotism."[21] The court then moved to a consideration of the second important question, a determination whether the state had demonstrated a "compelling state interest" that required that the defendant's rights under the first amendment be abridged. The key argument of the state revolved around the allegation that to allow some usage, even for religious purposes, would place upon its enforcement branch a tremendous burden because of the difficulty of detecting fraudulent claims of an asserted religious use of peyote. One argument was that there was a great threat to the indoctrination of small children; in reply to this the court pointed to the trial record, which showed that the Indian children never used the peyote, although teenagers did use the drug occasionally. The State also argued that the "peyote could be regarded as a symbol, one which obstructs enlightenment and shackles the Indian to primitive conditions," and that the state had a duty to eliminate its use. To this argument the court replied,

"We know of no doctrine that the state, in its asserted omniscience, should undertake to deny to defendants the observance of their religion in order to force them from the superstitious 'shackles' of their 'unenlightened' and 'primitive' conditions."[22]

As for the polygamy cases, which were pleaded as key support for the prosecution's position, the California court was quick to point out that the Supreme Court of the United States viewed the practice as highly injurious to its female adherents and classed polygamy with such religious rites as sacrifice of human beings and funeral immolation of widows, and of polygamy showed that the condemnation of the practice was a matter of the greatest social importance. It also found in polygamy the seed of destruction of a democratic society, and significantly held that polygamy, although a basic tenet in the theology of Mormonism, was not essential to the practice of the religion. Peyote, on the other hand, is the *sine qua non* of the Indian religion.

The final paragraph of the court's decision presents a beautifully written commentary on the tremendous difficulties faced when one tries to weigh the central practice of a religious faith against the demands of a conglomerate society.

> We know that some will urge that it is more important to subsume the rigorous enforcement of the narcotic laws than to carve out of them an exception for a few believers in a strange faith. They will say that the exception may produce problems of enforcement and that the dictate of the state must overcome the beliefs of a minority of Indians. But the problems of enforcement here do not directly differ from those of other situations which call for the detection of fraud. On the other hand, the right to free religious expression embodies a precious heritage of our history. In a mass society, which presses at every point towards conformity, the protection of a self-expression, however unique, of the individual and the group becomes even more important. The varying currents of the subcultures that flow into the mainstream of our national life give it depth and beauty. We preserve a greater value than an ancient tradition when we protect the rights of the Indians who honestly practiced an old religion in using peyote one night at a meeting in a desert hogan near Needles, California.[23]

The Woody case is recounted in depth, because it is the case that is most closely analogous to that which could be made on behalf of LSD. There have been serious experiments in which genuine religious experiences have been reported by those who have used LSD. Those experiences have been produced in both religious and non-religious persons and in both religious and non-religious settings, although there has naturally been a much higher percentage of genuine religious experiences among those who are religious and who take the drug in a religious setting. Dr. Walter H. Clark of the Andover-Newton Theological School has stated, "There is no doubt in my mind and in the minds of most religious scholars who have studied the question openmindedly—and a surprising number have tried the drug themselves—that under proper conditions LSD can release a profound religious experience."[24] Dr. Clark cited a controlled experiment at one school in which ten theological students were given placebos and ten a psychedelic drug before attending a religious service. Among the ten who received the actual drug, nine showed unmistakeable signs of profound experience, though in the other group only one indicated any symptom of a "mystical" experience.

Nonetheless, there are essential differences between peyote as used by the Indians of the Native American Church and LSD as used by those who subscribe to the League for Spiritual Discovery and the other psychedelic religious cults. Perhaps the most important difference is that LSD is only a means by which a religious experience can be achieved. First, it is not worshipped as a sacrament in its own right, and it is not the cornerstone of an entire religious sect. It is a medium or catalyst rather than an object of piety. Second, the careful controls present in the "meeting" setting are often not present in the taking of LSD, even at the sessions that have religion as their keynote. Last, there is no carefully controlled and circumscribed group using the drug; the users are often young people of diverse backgrounds, many of whom are seeking only a new thrill rather than taking part in a genuine religious experience. It is very doubtful that the Supreme Court of California, or any court, would recognize the LSD users as a *bona fide* religious cult unless the court could be shown that careful controls do in fact exist. There is the additional problem that LSD may perhaps inflict permanent damage upon its users. The court in the Woody case stated that in the opinion of scientists and other experts, peyote works no deleterious injury to the Indian. If use of LSD does in fact inflict genetic damage upon the user, a very different situation is presented.

At the Wesleyan symposium one very justifiable clamor of protest was raised. It revolved around a question to which an acceptable answer has not been provided: "Why is there so little research presently being done with LSD?" The question is a pivotal one, since there is now some evidence that LSD, if given under careful medical surveillance, may be potentially beneficial in the treatment of chronic alcoholism, sexual abnormalities, schizophrenia in children, psychoneurosis and psychopathy as well as in easing the effects of terminal diseases. Dr. Louria, one of the principal proponents for strict regulation of LSD, has stated, "These potential medical uses establish LSD as a drug which could in the future be of immense benefit to the medical profession."[25] The number of research projects have been relatively few, and the drug is dispensed for research only after an often tortuous task by the would-be researcher.

The entire legitimate supply of LSD is now in the hands of the National Institute of Mental Health, a unit of the Public Health Service of the Department of Health, Education and Welfare. This unit, in addition to possessing the drug, is also the granting agency, which provides a great deal of the financial support of research in the field of mental health. The National Institute of Mental Health is very slow to approve research projects employing LSD, even when the subjects are animals rather than humans; and approval of research projects with LSD on human subjects is extremely rare. Thus the researcher faces major hurdles in getting the drug to begin with, even if he has financial support from some other source, and an even more difficult task if he wishes to get *both* the drug and financial support from the National Institute of Mental Health. Once he has secured financial support and the drug, he faces yet a third hurdle, the Food and Drug Administration. Since LSD is not yet an approved drug, the prospective researcher must file an investigational new drug application (IND) with the Food and Drug Administration. This is a rigorous procedure, and added to the rigorous procedure of securing the drug and financial support from the N.I.M.H., it becomes an almost impossible task actually to commence research with LSD. Milton H. Joffe, of the Bureau of Drug Abuse Control of the Food and Drug Administration, has already stated, "The use of these drugs in research is reasonably plain, although I must admit that certain administrative procedures and coördination between F.D.A. and N.I.M.H. have not been reduced to the smoothest operation in the world." There is a great deal of truth in the accusation that meaningful research with LSD has been greatly retarded by the failure of coördination by these two controlling agencies.

In addition to administrative difficulties, there are other problems present in research generally and in research with LSD in particular. The furor began in 1964 when a group of doctors at the Jewish Chronic Disease Hospital in Brooklyn implanted live cancer cells into the bodies of terminal patients, patients who were dying of diseases other than cancer. The goal was to see if the body rejected the implanted cancer cells, a very important experiment, but done without the full and informed consent of the patients, who were never told that cancer cells were being implanted into their bodies. By the definition of "full and informed consent" is meant the consent of an individual after he has been made aware of and understands the major risks of a procedure. This is rather difficult if the subject is a catatonic schizophrenic.

A hospital trustee who had suspected that something serious was happening in the hospital demanded to see the records of these patients; his demand was refused by the administrator of the hospital. The trustee went to court and under court order examined the records and found what had occurred. The result of this and other reported research improprieties was a re-evaluation of research methods and procedures, particularly concerning the question of informed consent. The Public Health Service, on February 8, 1966, issued a statement requiring various precautions to insure that full consent is given and that the welfare of the subject is constantly protected. The statement, referring to all research and research-training grants supported by the Public Health Service, required a group review independent of the principal investigator of the project, with reference to the following questions: (1) the rights and welfare of the individuals involved; (2) the appropriateness of the methods used to obtain informed consent; and (3) the risks and potential medical benefits of the investigations. The review has to be made by an interdisciplinary committee independent of the principal investigators.

Grave problems are presented in securing the informed consent of mentally ill persons such as schizophrenics and of terminal patients whose minds are boggled as a result of disease or senility. The question of the appointment of guardians or next of kin who can and will give consent for research use of substances like LSD on such persons is also fraught with difficulty. There are grave doubts in the minds of many persons that a guardian can give consent for research procedures to be performed on his ward.

Subsequent modifications of this Public Health Service statement have broadened the categories of research that can be done without the full and informed consent of the subject. These modifications are along the lines of permitting the supervising physician more latitude if the research involves only social or behavioral investigation. The statement does reiterate, however, that grant use must be overseen and carefully reviewed by the committee "where a procedure may induce in the subject an altered state or condition potentially harmful to his personal welfare. Surgical procedures, the administration of drugs, the requirement of strenuous physical exertion . . . are examples of experimental arrangements which require thorough scrutiny by institutional review groups."[26] Perhaps there will be evolved more latitude for the physician, if he believes that the substance will more probably than not prove to be of therapeutic value to his patient. And perhaps LSD may someday be considered in this category. At the present time, however, because of administrative problems and the various restrictions placed upon research procedure, the road to research with LSD is hardly a smooth one.

The use of LSD by students and other young people constitutes a serious problem, for among this group there is the least control in use of the drug. The question of informed consent is relevant here, even when a *bona fide* research project is involved. The researcher who works with persons under the age of twenty-one works at his peril, because there is the question whether under the law a person under the age of twenty-one can give consent for research with a substance such as LSD. There is a movement to allow persons of the age of understanding to consent to surgical procedures, rather than retaining the formal age of twenty-one years, but most jurisdictions have not formally allowed such a change. Research with LSD would probably be in the same category as surgical procedure. At the present time, however, parental consent should be obtained before research is done with persons under the age of twenty-one. In all probability this would be required by both the F.D.A. and the N.I.M.H.

LSD poses a far greater problem than carefully controlling *bona fide* research with young people. This is the problem of controlling the use of the illicitly obtained substance by those of college age or younger. The attraction to the drug is very great, and it is no surprise that this is so with paragraphs like the following appearing in widely read magazines such as *Playboy:*

> When Dr. Goddard, the head of the Food and Drug Administration announced in a senate hearing that ten percent of our college students are taking LSD, did you ever wonder why? Sure, they're discovering God and meaning; sure, they're discovering themselves; but did you really think that sex wasn't the fundamental reason for this surging, youthful social boom? You can no more do research on LSD and leave out ecstasy than you can do microscopic research on tissue and leave out cells.[27]

One of the groups that has been struggling hardest with the problem of LSD usage is college administrators, genuinely and justifiably concerned with the illicit use of LSD on campus. The following is excerpted from a statement by John U. Munro, the Dean of Harvard College:

> As anyone bright enough to be at Harvard knows perfectly well, possession or distribution of marijuana and LSD are strictly against the law, and taking the drugs involves users in psychological dangers and contacts with the criminal underworld. The college is prepared to take disciplinary action up to and including dismissal against any student found to be involved in the use or distribution of illegal and dangerous drugs. In sum, if a student is stupid enough to misuse his time here fooling around with illegal and dangerous drugs, our view is that he should leave college and make room for people prepared to take good advantage of the college opportunity.[28]

It is questionable whether this statement does very much to

counter the sense of adventure promised by Mr. Leary in adding the threat of expulsion to the already harsh punishments imposed by the criminal law. Dean Munro's statement was accompanied by an excellent summary of the deleterious medical aspects of LSD, and the colleges do have a definite duty to alert their student bodies to the dangers inherent in the drug. The most effective means of prevention of illicit use lies in the wide publication of such knowledge, combined with the availability of services, psychiatric and other, to which the student can turn if he feels the need to do so. Individual contacts by persons knowledgeable in the field of drug abuse and understanding the student are among the most effective means of dealing with the problem. The instituting of seminars on drug abuse, if properly designed and presented, is another way to approach the problem on a sophisticated and meaningful plane.

College officials are also faced with interesting and difficult legal questions relative to the search and seizure of dangerous drugs found on campus. The forcing of a dormitory door and the seizing of the drugs by the campus police may have the salutory effects of providing a good scare for the offending students and at the same time preventing prosecution and possible felony convictions because of improper search and seizure of the evidence. It is most important for the college administration and the campus security officials to maintain a working and understanding relationship with the municipal and state police as well as the federal officials. Guidelines should be worked out to prevent insofar as possible the prosecution of students, while at the same time preventing wholesale student violation of the law.

LSD provides challenges to every level of our society. It is a great challenge to medicine, which must treat those who have been severely injured by uncontrolled use of the drug, and at the same time must strive for research so that the full potential of the drug may become known and realized. It is a great challenge to the law, which must prevent persons from injuring themselves through improper and uncontrolled use, yet must permit and encourage meaningful research. The law accomplishes very little when the only result is to make felons of young people seeking a new thrill. The many challenges can and must be met, and all of us, lawyers, physicians and educators, must work together in meeting them.

LSD LEGISLATION

AUTHOR'S NOTE: Because many state legislatures convene only every other year, and because any legislation involving LSD that has been passed in the current 1967 session would not be officially reported until after the compilation of this chart, it is difficult to present a current nationwide picture of such legislation. The situation is further complicated by states that may deal with LSD by unreported regulations rather than by specific legislation. This chart was prepared by Robert Scott Lingley, a third-year student at the Law School of Boston University.

State	Category of the law concerning LSD	Penalty for illegal use	Penalty for illegal sale	Penalty for illegal manu- facture	Penalty for illegal possession	Penalty for illegal sale to minors	Exemption for research purposes
Alabama	No provision for LSD as of the 1965 legislative session.						
Alaska	No provision for LSD as of 1966.						
Arizona Tit. 32, Ch. 18 1967 Leg. Ses.	LSD treated in ch. on dang. drugs.	First offense: up to 1 yr. jail; $1000 fine. Sub- sequent: 1-10 yr. &/or $5000.	1-15 yr. &/ or up to $10,000.	Mfr. not illegal.	Up to 1 yr. &/ or up to $1,000.	No provi- sion.	No excep- tion for research.
Arkansas	No mention of LSD as of 1965 legislative session.						

LSD LEGISLATION (Continued)

State	Category of the law concerning LSD	Penalty for illegal use	Penalty for illegal sale	Penalty for illegal manufacture	Penalty for illegal possession	Penalty for illegal sale to minors	Exemption for research purposes
California Hlth. & Sfty. Code § 11901-11916; 1966 Supp.	LSD treated as dang. drug in separate ch. by that name.	No provision.	First offense: 1-5, st. prison. Subsequent: 2-10, st. prison; see note 1 for limitations.	No provision.	Poss. & poss. w/ intent to sell = separate offenses; see note 1.	First offense: 1-5, st. prison. Subsequent: 2-10; see note 1.	Exception for research limited to "investigational use" by experts who are exempted by §§ 26228 & 26292 of Hlth. & Sfty. Code.
Colorado	No mention of LSD as of the 1963 legislative session.						

LSD LEGISLATION (Continued)

State	Category of the law concerning LSD	Penalty for illegal use	Penalty for illegal sale	Penalty for illegal manufacture	Penalty for illegal possesion	Penalty for illegal sale to minors	Exemption for research purposes
Connecticut	As a hallucinogen.	No provision.	$1,000 and/or 2 years for 1st offense	See column 3.	$1,000 or 1 year or both.	No provision.	Yes—see text.
Delaware	No mention of LSD as of the 1966 legislative session.						
District of Columbia	No specific mention of LSD, but see note 2.						
Florida Tit. 27, Ch. 404 §§ 404.01-404.15	Nothing on LSD as of April, 1967.						
Georgia	No mention of LSD as of the 1966 legislative session.						
Hawaii	No provision for LSD as of the 1963 legislative session.[3]						
Idaho	No provision for LSD as of the 1965 legislative session.						
Illinois	Nothing on LSD as of March, 1967.						
Indiana	Nothing on LSD as of the 1966 legislative session.						

LSD LEGISLATION (Continued)

State	Category of the law concerning LSD	Penalty for illegal use	Penalty for illegal sale	Penalty for illegal manufacture	Penalty for illegal possession	Penalty for illegal sale to minors	Exemption for research purposes
Iowa	No provision for LSD as of 1966.						
Kansas	No provision for LSD as of the 1965 legislative session, although Kansas does have a hypnotic-drug act.						
Kentucky	No provision for LSD as of the first session of 1967.						
Louisiana La. Civil Code Tit. 40 §§ 1031-1046 1966 Supp.	Defined as hallucinogenic drug.	No provision.	First offense: up to 2 yr. &/or $1000. Subsequent: up to 5 yr. &/or $5000.	None for mfr.	Same as for sale; see column 3.	Up to 10 yrs.	Yes; very liberal; any person engaged in lawful research.
Maine	No provision for LSD as of 1965.						

LSD LEGISLATION (Continued)

State	Category of the law concerning LSD	Penalty for illegal use	Penalty for illegal sale	Penalty for illegal manufacture	Penalty for illegal possession	Penalty for illegal sale to minors	Exemption for research purposes
Massachusetts[4] Mass. G.L. Ann. §§ 197-217e 1966 Supp.	Treated as narc. drug w/ marijuana & heroin.	No provision.	First offense: 5-10 yrs. Subsequent: 10-25 yrs.	First offense: $500-1000 or 6 mo. to 2 yrs. Second: $500-1000 or 5-10 yrs. Subsequent: $2000 and 10-20 yrs.	St. prison up to 3½ yrs; or hse. of corr. up to 2½ yrs. or up to $1000.	No separate penalty for sale to minor; see note 5.	Yes; to a person in *charge* of laboratory only, & only for use in that laboratory.
Michigan Mich. Stat. Ann. Tit. 18 § 18.1106 1966 Supp.	Treated w/ hypnotic drugs.	No provision.	See note 6.	No provision.	See note 6.	No separate provision.	There is an exemption in accordance w/ Fed. Food, Drug & Cosmetic Act.

LSD LEGISLATION (Continued)

State	Category of the law concerning LSD	Penalty for illegal use	Penalty for illegal sale	Penalty for illegal manufacture	Penalty for illegal possession	Penalty for illegal sale to minors	Exemption for research purposes
Minnesota	Nothing on LSD as of the first session for 1967.						
Mississippi Tit. 25, § 6844-6846 1966 Supp.	Defined as narc. drug w/marijuana.	No prohibition against use.	First offense: 5-10 yrs. & up to $2000. Subsequent: life impr.	First: 2-5 & up to $2000. Second: 5-10 yrs. & up to $2000. Third: 10-20 & up to $2000.	Same as for mfr. See column 4.	Up to life impris. & up to $20,000.	Yes. § 6849.
Missouri	No provision for LSD as of February, 1967.						
Montana	No provision for LSD as of the 1965 legislative session.						
Nebraska	Nothing on LSD as of the 1965 legislative session.						
Nevada	Nothing on LSD as of the 1965 legislature.						

LSD LEGISLATION (Continued)

State	Category of the law concerning LSD	Penalty for illegal use	Penalty for illegal sale	Penalty for illegal manu-facture	Penalty for illegal possession	Penalty for illegal sale to minors	Exemption for research purposes
New Hamp-shire N.H. General Laws Ann. Ch. 318-A, §§ 318-A:1 to A:26 (1967 Supp.).	Treated as a narco-tic drug.	No provi-sion.	$2,000 and 2-5 years for first offense; $2,000 and 5-10 for 2nd offense; $2,000 and 10-20 years for 3rd offense.	Same as column 3.	Same as column 3.	No provi-sion.	No provi-sion.
New Jersey	No specific mention of LSD, but see note 7.						
New Mexico	No specific mention of LSD, but see note 8.						

LSD LEGISLATION (Continued)

State	Category of the law concerning LSD	Penalty for illegal use	Penalty for illegal sale	Penalty for illegal manufacture	Penalty for illegal possession	Penalty for illegal sale to minors	Exemption for research purposes
New York Penal Code § 1747-d 1966 Supp.	Defined as hallucinogenic drug.	No provision.	First: up to 1 yr. &/or $500. Subsequent: up to 2 yr. &/or up to $1000.	No provision.	Same penalty as sale; see column 3.	No separate provision.	Only licensed physicians & licensed mfrs. w/ special permission are exempt.
No. Carolina	No specific mention of LSD, but see note 9.						
No. Dakota	No provision as of the 1965 legislative session.						
Ohio	No provision on LSD as of 1966.						
Oklahoma	No provision on LSD as of May, 1967.						
Oregon	No provision on LSD as of the 1965 legislative session.						
Pennsylvania	No provision as of 1966, although Pennsylvania has a hypnotic-drug act.						

LSD LEGISLATION (Continued)

State	Category of the law concerning LSD	Penalty for illegal use	Penalty for illegal sale	Penalty for illegal manufacture	Penalty for illegal possession	Penalty for illegal sale to minors	Exemption for research purposes
Rhode Island	Defined and treated as a narcotic drug.						
So. Carolina	No specific mention of LSD, but see note 10.						
So. Dakota	No provision for LSD as of 1966, but see note 11.						
Tennessee	Nothing on LSD as of 1966.						
Texas	No mention of LSD as of the 1966 legislative session.						
Utah	No provision as of 1965.						
Vermont	No mention of LSD as of the 1966 legislative session.						
Virginia	No specific mention of LSD, but see note 12.						
Washington Ch. 71 § 69.40-.060.	Treated & defined as dang. drug.	No provision.	Up to 6 mo. impr. &/ or up to $200 fine.	No provision.	See note 13.	No provision.	
W. Virginia	No provision for LSD as of the 1966 legislative session.						
Wisconsin	Nothing on LSD as of the 1966 legislative session.						
Wyoming	Nothing on LSD as of the 1965 legislative session.						

NOTES: LSD LEGISLATION (chart)

1. For possession the penalty is one year imprisonment and/or $1000 for the first offense. For subsequent offenses it is 1-5 years in state prison or up to one year in the county jail, only if the previous conviction is charged in the indictment and if found true by a jury or by a judge.

Possession with intent to sell is made a separate offense: 1-3 years in state prison or up to one year in the county jail for the first offense. Subsequent offenses bring from 2-10 years in state prison, with the same limitation as above.

2. In addition to the amphetamines and barbiturates, the term "dangerous drug" is defined in the District of Columbia as "other drugs or compounds, preparations or mixtures thereof which the Commissioners shall find and declare by rule or regulation duly promulgated, after reasonable public notice and opportunity for a hearing, to be habit forming, excessively stimulating, or to have a dangerously toxic or hypnotic or somnifacient effect on the body of a human or animal." [§33-701] LSD might be covered by such a ruling not published in the official code.

3. There is no published supplement after that covering the 1963 legislative session.

4. Massachusetts has a provision making it illegal to be present where LSD is illegally kept or deposited, or to be in the company of a person, knowing that said person is illegally in possession of LSD. The penalty is imprisonment for up to 5 years in the state prison, or two years in a house of correction, or a fine of between $500 and $5000.

5. There is a separate penalty for inducing or attempting to induce a minor to use LSD, except in accordance with a valid prescription. The penalty for the first offense is imprisonment in state prison for 10-25 years; for subsequent offenses, 20-50 years.

6. Michigan makes the sale, possession or disposition of LSD a felony, but nowhere in the hypnotic-drug act is there defined what constitutes a felony.

7. A stimulant or depressant drug is defined to include any drug which the secretary of health shall find by regulation as having a potential for abuse because of its hallucinogenic effect on the central nervous system. See §24:6C-1(3).

8. Under its Drugs and Cosmetics Act, the New Mexico Board of Pharmacy has the power to make additions or deletions to its list of dangerous drugs as it may deem necessary. These additions would not appear in the official statutes.

9. §90-113.1(1) of the North Carolina statutes defines barbiturate drugs as those drugs which are found by the Board of Pharmacy as having a hypnotic or somnifacient effect on the human body, and duly promulgated by rule or regulation.

10. South Carolina has a provision in its stimulant or depressant

drug act allowing the State Department of Health to find by regulation that any substance having a hallucinogenic effect on the central nervous system is a depressing or stimulating drug.

11. The latest supplement available for South Dakota was that of 1960.

12. §54-446.3(3) of the Virginia statutes defines a depressant or stimulant drug as including any drug which has a potential for abuse because of its hallucinogenic effect on the central nervous system. However, this must be found by the Board after investigation, and must be promulgated by regulation.

13. The penalty for illegal possession is that for a "gross misdemeanor," but there is no indication that a gross misdemeanor calls for a greater penalty than a misdemeanor, which brings imprisonment up to 6 months and/or a fine of up to $200.

REFERENCES: SOURCES CITED IN TEXT

1. "Hallucinogens: A Growing Problem in Indiscriminate Use," from *The Medicated Society*, a Lowell Lecture Series of Tufts Medical Center, by Donald B. Louria, M.D.
2. Mass. Gen. Laws Ann. Ch. 94 §213A. (1966 Supp.).
3. *Ibid.* §212A.
4. *Ibid.* §212B.
5. *Ibid.* §210A.
6. New Hampshire Revised Statutes Ann. §318-A:1, ¶IX, (1967 Supp.)
7. Public Act #555, §1(13), 1967 Legislature.
8. *Ibid.* §37(b).
9. *Ibid.* §40(a).
10. *Ibid.* §49(a).
11. *Ibid.* §68.
12. *Ibid.* §61.
13. 31 Federal Register 1076, §166.1.
14. *Leary vs. United States,* U.S. District Court of Appeals for the Fifth Circuit, Brief for Appellant, p. 2.
15. *Late Corporation of Latter-Day Saints v. United States,* 136 US 1 (1890); see also *Cleveland v. United States,* 329 US 14, 16 (1946).
16. *Leary* Brief, *op. cit.,* p. 37.
17. *Ibid.*
18. *People v. Woody,* 40 Cal. Reptr. 69, 394 P.2d 813, 815 (1964).
19. *Ibid.* p. 813.
20. *Ibid.* p. 812.
21. *Ibid.* p. 818.
22. *Ibid.*
23. *Ibid.* p. 821, 822.
24. Boston *Sunday Herald,* April 30, 1967, p. 18.

25. "Hallucinogens: A Growing Problem in Indiscriminate Use," from *The Medicated Society,* a Lowell Lecture Series of Tufts Medical Center, by Donald B. Louria, M. D., p. 3.
26. Statement of the U. S. Public Health Service, Division of Research Grants, December 12, 1966.
27. *Playboy,* Vol. 13, No. 9, September, 1966, p. 100.
28. Boston *Globe,* Saturday, April 15, 1967, p. 4.

8 Second Discussion

The moderator: The psychedelic drugs have often been referred to as an instrument for conversion, with use centered on the college campuses. Many articles about LSD seem to stress the college campuses. Of course, Greenwich Village is essentially in the watershed of New York University and other universities there, and the Berkeley scene is close to the Berkeley campus. On the other hand, it has been suggested that the spread of LSD is an autonomous phenomenon, not related to the college community. I would like to ask the members of the panel to speak to this. Is the LSD phenomenon in our culture today a college-bound phenomenon or is it, in fact, independent and autonomous?

Dr. Pahnke: I would say that Dr. Louria's figures from this afternoon would dispute that, because he showed that it was used by people with all kinds of occupations, not only by students. I think that 15% were students. I'm not sure that use was ever confined to colleges.

Dr. Louria: The Blum studies show us the same thing exactly, but far more precisely than the few data from our hospital.

A member of the audience: I have a suggestion to make, and I'd like to ask both Mr. Joffe and Dr. Pahnke whether it's feasible. Everybody is agreed that more research is needed. The problem seems to be that today and tomorrow and the next few weeks a lot of kids and others are going to be turning on, and a small, yet unknown proportion of these are going to be harmed. I would like to suggest that perhaps the people from Spring Grove could get together with the people from the government to the extent that they have techniques worked out, to the extent that any bit of information that could be provided to the community at large to help people use whatever research there has been and to prevent people from harming themselves. I think that this might be useful. So that the proportion, whether it is one in a thousand or one in ten thousand, goes down. And that something be done relatively soon to try to alleviate the problem as it exists.

Mr. Joffe: Dr. Louria has already given you the answer this afternoon. He said don't use it; it's a dangerous drug.

Same member of the audience: But people are not listening, though it is a dangerous drug, because of the kinds of evidence referred to today. People think that they can use it, taking the proper precautions themselves; and these people are trying to decide for themselves whether they can handle it.

Mr. Joffe: Do you suggest that each individual who would like to try the drug furnish a complete medical history, including electroencephalograms and psychiatric interview, which is the only way I know of to be reasonably sure that the individual will not have a bad reaction?

Same member of the audience: I think that there appears a general principle for dealing with the LSD experience that seems to be implied in what Dr. Pahnke said, and I am asking whether such things couldn't be made available to the public, because some segment of the public is going to experiment regardless of what anyone says.

The moderator: I'm not clear on just what you're proposing. It sounds to me as though you're proposing something that we thought we were getting at when we set up this symposium, that is, providing definitive information on which people can base their decisions. This is one thing, but I think that there is inherent in what you are saying a second suggestion, which is that there be set up essentially some instrument for providing a mechanism of screening. I don't know what that would be.

Same member of the audience: I am talking about procedures for guiding people on trips. To the extent that such procedures— and Dr. Pahnke stressed the importance of this—seem to be the prime determinant as to whether a person has or has not a favorable experience.

Dr. Pahnke: Let me comment. Such procedures have been worked out at Spring Grove and are continuing to be. They will be published in the scientific literature, but that will take time, at least a couple of years. If what you want actually happened, if you did have the information now, and it was disseminated, I don't think it would help too much because other researchers couldn't, perhaps, get the permission to use the drug anyway. You want it for the lay people. In a handbook?

Same member of the audience: For the people whom Dr. Louria is worried about.

Dr. Pahnke: But you see, they wouldn't be using it under medical guidance, which is the essential point.

Dr. Louria: I think we're in a real dilemma. You see, the whole thing is that there are several levels involved. On the one hand, there's the research problem, and during the evening I was just figuring out from the Congressional hearings what the research situation is. And here is what it is, if my figures are at all accurate. In 1964 there were about seventy licensed investigators; in 1965, thirty-nine; in 1966, thirty-one; and currently, *only* sixteen. As to N.I.M.H. funds, there was available in 1964 1.5 million dollars; in 1965, 1.49 million dollars; in 1965, 927,000 dollars, a decrease of over one-third in one year; and currently there is still less available. It is abundantly clear that research has been markedly reduced; and you can prove this fact with the government's own figures. Now, that's one level, research that we desperately want to increase. And I don't think that there is any excuse for the N.I.M.H. not to increase it.

Then, there's the second level, which is the kind of research that you are doing, Dr. Kurland, absolutely well controlled and under medical aegis. We all want that increased. That has to be increased. That's very important research. And there's the third level, research in a broader context, in a community that may be in your semi-utopian future under some control. And there's the fourth level, the level that you're talking about, namely, having people take the drug, young people, unprepared, on their own. That level is the one that bothers me. I am not bothered by the other three levels. There is no way of disseminating information *now* to that fourth group and to prevent their having adverse reactions. That group, young, unprepared, under uncontrolled conditions, that group is the one that we are desperately trying to educate *not* to take the drug in any circumstances, because it is not one in a thousand or one in ten thousand. At the very minimum it is several per cent. Now, the derivative problem is that of that several per cent who do get into trouble, certain ones are going to do very dramatic things. They are going to jump out windows or walk in front of cars, enough to get front-page headlines. In New York City 1% of heroin addicts die every year of an overdose.

This fact almost never gets headlines, because it isn't very dramatic. They shoot the stuff into their veins, and they drop dead. They are taken to the coroner's office. We whisk them off to the grave, and nobody cares. But let somebody jump out a window under LSD, the way the newspapers are now, and that's front-page across the country.

In doing that, what you do is to arouse not the people who are interested in LSD, a very small segment of the population, but what Leary has called the middle-class, middle-aged monolith that runs our country. I'm not derogating that, for I'm rather for their running the country. This relatively stable group then transmits its fears and angers and anxieties to legislatures, which are dependent on this middle-aged monolith for their maintenance in office, and you know what happens. So the only way by which you can avoid more restrictive laws, which make the whole situation worse, is by getting the fourth group off its LSD kick. I think that we have to have some laws, both federal and state, to help us in that endeavor; because if you don't, then you will destroy the other three levels— from animal research to human research to community research, all of which could be of enormous value to all of us in the future.

The moderator: Are there any questions from the floor?

A member of the audience: It seems to me that a lot of people have forgotten the fact that the reason people are dropping out is because their society wants them to drop out. Dr. Pahnke, what do you think that the possibilities are that at some time in the future, people won't drop out, but will work to change the aspects of society that tend to drive them out?

Dr. Pahnke: I think that would be fine. I am a little concerned as to what happens to these people who do drop out. Who is really helping them? I know what happens to some of the people who drop out, because we get them as patients in our out-patient clinic. These are people who before they took LSD had, perhaps, some problems and were told that they needed psychotherapy, but they would have none of it. They felt that they were quite healthy and that their advisers were just talking through their hats. They took LSD, got very shaken up and perhaps dropped out of school. But then they come to the clinic seeking therapy, and, paradoxically enough, these people are then quite eager to work in therapy. This is a danger that has a paradoxical, perhaps good, effect, but I certainly would not recommend it as a way of getting into therapy.

A member of the audience: There was an earlier question concerning black-market impurities and the dangers of them. Would Mr. Joffe discuss this?

Mr. Joffe: I'm afraid I can't tell you what the impurities might be. There is some black-market material that is of exceedingly good quality. I don't mean to say that everything that is not legitimate is of poor quality. We do know, however, that a simple analysis of a cube will show perhaps 30% of LSD; it will also show on an ultraviolet spectrum many peaks that you know are not LSD and do not occur in the pure product. Therefore they are impurities of one sort or another. It has not seemed too important to our activities to find out what is wrong with this product or that product, because they are *all* illegal. I don't see what good it will do us to run the analyses of the home-made products so that someone will know that there is bad in his product.

Dr. Pahnke: Unless he were getting heroin or something else. That should be publicized, I think. It might deter some people from taking it. I've heard of that happening. Amphetamines, barbiturates and heroin do get mixed in with LSD. I think this could have very bad effects in terms of persons' becoming addicted.

Mr. Joffe: These are recognizable peaks on an ultraviolet absorption spectrum.

Dr. Pahnke: Yes, but if you're not making an analysis, how would you know that?

Mr. Joffe: You run the curve, and you see that here is the peak that we know is LSD. . .

Dr. Pahnke: Yes, that's fine, if you're doing them, but you said that you're not doing them.

Mr. Joffe: No, I said we're not running the peak down to find out what the impurity is.

Dr. Pahnke: Well, say the impurity was heroin? Somebody had added . . .

Mr. Joffe: Heroin has a recognizable peak.

Dr. Pahnke: One that is easily recognized?

Mr. Joffe: Yes.

Dr. Pahnke: Do you find that?

Mr. Joffe: I don't know. I have not myself heard of it.

The moderator: I'm afraid that some of you couldn't hear the discussion that went on at the table. Let me try to paraphrase it quickly for you. Dr. Pahnke asked the question if it wasn't a social

responsibility of the F.D.A. to check out the actual nature of
impurities to forestall possibly the use of drugs such as heroin as
additives to sugar cubes and therefore make this public knowledge
in order to warn people who might use them.

A member of the audience: I am not satisfied with a previous
answer. LSD appeals to young people, and what's to prevent their
using it? You agree that something should be done to stop free
usage by young people. You refuse to recognize any valid reason
for using LSD regardless of whether the user be a young student
or a middle-aged person. I think there is a responsibility among
all groups, doctors, psychiatrists and legal people, to recognize that
there is going to be a lot of illegal LSD usage. In light of the circumstances, what can be done to keep the number of bad trips
down? This is a problem. The refusal to offer any kind of guidance
to users is bad.

The moderator: As I understand the question, it says, as a
banner did over the Sather Gate at the University of California
recently, "Never trust anybody over thirty." We are being accused,
I guess, of evading the issue that has been brought before us, which
is that there is a large population of people who fall into category
four, as defined earlier by Dr. Louria, those who use LSD on their
own in situations in which there is no guidance. The panel is asked
to comment on possible ways of minimizing bad trips, psychotic
episodes and hospital admissions for this category.

Mr. Chayet: I think that this is one of the basic defenses for
the existing laws. As I understand these gentlemen who are
certainly the professionals in dealing with LSD, there is no way to
give out information on a mass scale to tell you how to take LSD
on your own. Even Mr. Leary has suggested that there be licensing
of individuals. He wants, of course, to reduce the criteria for getting
a license to work with LSD; and he certainly doesn't believe in the
medical profession's having exclusive control. But even Mr. Leary
says that there should be some control and some guidance; and as I
understand it, there is just no way of preparing a brochure so that
you can do it yourself and be successful at it, though I would be
interested to hear if this is a possibility.

Mr. Joffe: I think that the question ultimately boils down to
the fact that the gentleman says that there will be the use of this
drug whether we authorize it or not. There will also be bank

robberies, murders and other crimes whether we have laws or not. What you are asking us to do is to show you the best way to evade the law. You want the government to furnish the safecracker with tools to make his job easier. We can't do this. It is not a province of a regulatory agency to show people how to evade the law. Aside from the fact that there is no cookbook sort of thing for this.

Dr. Pahnke: Well, actually, there are some manuals.

Mr. Joffe: But not for the ordinary individual.

Dr. Pahnke: Well, yes.

Mr. Joffe: One off the street?

Dr. Pahnke: Yes. Actually, this is what Leary proposed when he founded IF-IF. He was going to write a number of manuals. He wrote two, and *The Psychedelic Experience* has nearly a chapter describing how to run a session. The trouble is that you cannot learn this from a book. What you need is specialized training, in which you work under someone or watch someone run sessions, as it is possible at Spring Grove, where there is a closed-circuit television system. But this is not yet set up to train a lot of people, though it might be possible sometime in the future. This is what I suggested, having training centers, but we're a long way from that. So for the present time I can't offer you any advice. These manuals may be somewhat helpful, but I certainly don't think that that's the way to learn how to use LSD.

Same member of the audience: My question asked for the recognition that there is going to be a lot of usage by the layman. Instead of saying merely that this is something to be outlawed, leaving it at that and limiting research to laboratory settings, you are asked to shift from your concern with developing a definite set of rules and direct your attention toward existing problems. Perhaps there's something that should be outlawed. But users of LSD have a right to be considered themselves.

The moderator: I will say that I believe many people in our culture, in our nation and in the western nations whom I know and have talked to are very concerned about this. As I understand the question, we are being asked to increase at least the amount of attention that we are paying to that group, group four, people who are taking LSD on their own, and to share our attention with them, the same attention that animal research receives. I think that's what you are asking us to do.

Dr. Pahnke: I would just like to say in addition that it takes three to six months to train adequately an LSD therapist, to have him learn how to deal with all possible contingencies, so that he can really guide people with safety. It's no thing that you can learn easily just from a few rules. Some people have gone ahead on their own and had experiences, and there have been a lot of bad experiences. These people of the lay public have learned by experience, and some have had some very bad trips. But I don't think that's the ideal way to do it. And you're right, it is a problem. Some people feel that we just suppress the problem by passing a law against it and assuming that this law will take care of it. I don't feel that it will, and I think that it will take time to work this out. If LSD does continue to spread, and more and more people do continue to take it, there will eventually be pressure to change the laws or to make some provision for this, but that also will take time. I know that this solution probably won't satisfy you. You want something right now. The reality is that it probably is not practical.

A member of the audience: Well, I see some sense of understanding among certain members of the panel who have spoken today, and I wonder whether the more legalistically oriented members of the panel are sitting with points of view that might be expressed by the statement "Well, we'll let the sympathetic people speak, but we've got the say, because we make the laws, we enforce them, we regulate them." Or whether, in fact, there is a sense of coöperation and understanding among the people who are gathered here to speak to us on the issue?

The moderator: But that precisely is the reason why we're doing it.

Same member of the audience: Yes, I know. I understand. My question, though, is whether in the process there are formulations going on?

Mr. Joffe: I am working for the Bureau of Drug Abuse Control, which you may call legalistically oriented, if you wish, but I am not a lawyer. I am not an enforcement agent. I am a pharmacologist. The reason that I am working for this agency is because it offers me a chance to get some scientific work done, and I am interested in the scientific aspects of this problem. But that the support happens to be in a bureau that has as well the responsibility for enforcement does not deter me. I am not going to try to change the rules of enforcement. This is something else. But I have joined them, because they give me an opportunity to do the scientific work that I want to see done. This is my personal approach to it. I can't speak for anyone else. We have the authority not only to do in-house research but also to have contract research done. When I say support for research, I don't mean that someone has to build me a ten-million-dollar laboratory. I have the authority to solicit or to receive unsolicited proposals from those individuals who would like to do work on drug abuse of a scientific nature that I am capable of supporting.

The moderator: I think that we have slipped away from the question, and rather than see this thread followed, I'd like the question to get the attention that I think it really deserves. I wasn't kidding when I said that one of the shocking signs of my life was the sign over the Sather Gate, which appeared in all the papers, saying "Never trust anybody over thirty." You know, that really gets at me. I don't know why. I need a lot of love, I guess, and I want people who are under thirty to believe somehow that even if I am not a part of their culture and don't understand them, I do *want* to understand them, and I think that this feeling is shared by many people who are my age and older. We are trying very hard to understand, and in addition to trying to understand we are trying to act in good faith. Now, in your question, as you phrased it, there was an implication that I hear very frequently—"Yes, you pay lip service to understanding, but actually you want to pass regulations and hold us down. You're afraid of us. We are coming up. We're new and we're different, and we threaten you." In a sense, that's true. It is the business of the young to displace the old. That's the story of life, but I would defend the people here today, all of us, the people who have been most militant in their expressions and those who seem most permissive, from the charge of insincerity. I don't think that these people are, and I certainly know that I am not, insincere.

Mr. Chayet: I would like to comment. I am under thirty, so I don't know where that really puts me. I'm also probably not a very good representative of the law-enforcement profession, because I don't like these laws. I think, however, that they are an absolute necessity. For example, the law regarding marijuana. I have grave doubt that anybody who is carrying around marijuana seed ought to get thirty years in prison. That bothers me very much, because it doesn't seem to me that the danger is there. I've heard from so many that alcohol is much more dangerous than marijuana, but this may be subject to rebuttal by those who know more about marijuana. It seems to me that when you talk about psilocybin and LSD, the danger is very great, and therefore we do need laws to protect people from themselves. I think that if the danger weren't there, that the laws would be bad and unnecessary. It's the danger that really necessitates the legislation. As soon as we have some control and some training centers, or anything else, I would be the first to want to see the laws go.

Dr. Louria: Well, I think that you really said what I was going to say, Mr. Chayet. I'm not sympathetic with the questioner's point of view. I think that we have shown you beyond peradventure that this drug, taken under those conditions that you want to take it under, is a dangerous drug. There's no question about that. You can't show me evidence that taken under your circumstances this gives you anything other than a kick. You can't show me that it gives you any lasting benefit, though it may. But that will come from the kind of research that Dr. Kurland is doing and Dr. Pahnke is doing and others will do if we can get more research on a broader level. Not from your going out with a do-it-yourself kit and taking LSD. Our medical view is simple. If you take it under those circumstances, you can't show anybody that it does you any good; and a certain percentage of you are going to end up in hospitals with acute or chronic psychoses; and some of you, infrequently, but some of you, are going to end up dead. We know that *now.* So what we're telling you is very simple. We do not under any conditions condone the concept or understand the concept or agree with any part of the concept that you ought to be able to take drugs like LSD—not marijuana—under these conditions and have us give to you a pamphlet that tells you how to do it better. As far as I'm concerned, if you're going to do it, knowing what the dangers are, you damn well take the risk; and if you get into trouble, what we will do in the medical profession is to publicize the adverse effects that you have in the hope that other people won't get into that trouble until the time when we do have the knowledge that it can be given to people, such as you, on an out-patient basis, relatively safely.

Mr. Barron: Well, I don't think that Dr. Louria's response answers the question, the intent of the question, as it was put. Also, I wish that Dr. Louria would speak for himself and not say "we." It seems you said, "We have shown you beyond a peradventure of a doubt." There has been a lack of imaginative or constructive attempts to find other means, other solutions, new institutions to meet what has been an expressed need on the part of a lot of people. I don't think that what one should do is to give advice on how to break the law. I think it's just what has to be built up as a body of opinion, reflecting pressure to create forms that will meet new social needs. It is not a matter just of restrictive laws.

Dr. Pahnke: At the end, Dr. Louria, you said if there was enough evidence accumulated showing that it was safe to give LSD on an out-patient basis, you would be for it. Now, what would that evidence consist of for you? How much evidence would you need? I think that there is some evidence already, but how much more do you need?

Dr. Louria: Under whose aegis?

Dr. Pahnke: I think that what they are doing at Spring Grove has shown that very sick patients can be given LSD without serious consequences, so far anyway, with almost two hundred patients.

Dr. Kurland: I think that the safety question is in everybody's mind, and the safety record established in research at Spring Grove didn't happen by chance. There were years of pilot work done by experts, by professionals in these drug studies; and before we initiated these control studies, there were pilot studies that went on a year or longer. The thing that I oppose is to let unsophisticated people, who don't have the longitudinal experience, who don't have all the things that one needs from the standpoint of physiological and behavioral background, to plunge into these areas and carry on research. The point is that without the necessary tools you can't even document what you are doing. You can't put this down in some kind of systematic way so that it can be replicated. The way that our studies started, the history of prior research in our area had to be studied in order to work out a plan. We didn't just plunge into this. We gathered the reports that came from the different investigators, and we formulated the usefulness of treatment of alcoholics. These were very full reports. We started out by attempting to replicate these things, and this is our point for beginning to learn. For people who say that they can get something accomplished in uncontrolled studies, who think that they are going to get a lot of new information and insight, I would just bring back to your attention the fact that we first had to learn something about what goes on in group psychotherapy, where there aren't many complicating conditions. So, with all due respect to the younger people, it is very, very important to learn the rules before you get involved; certainly they would refuse to allow anybody to get into the field of radioactivity without having a license indicating technical competency.

Mr. Barron: Let me make it quite clear that I am not, by any means, advocating usage of any of these substances that are illegal. What I was saying is that I think that the intent or motive of the question was misinterpreted and that what is essentially threatening is some kind of feeling that the present laws and present social institutions are not adequate to a deeply felt need on the part of some people. It's this, I think, that should be taken seriously, as a feeling, and that if we use all of it, we will work as best we can and create whatever kinds of institutions are necessary, if indeed it's true that this is no passing fad and represents something that is important to the general movement of mind over the past fifty years.

The moderator: Let me say that it was my feeling that in your paper, Mr. Barron, you tried to provide an historical analysis for this anomie toward which the question was directed. I felt that that was a matter of record today, and I was including you among those of us who feel sincerely concerned about these problems.

A member of the audience: Well, I hope that the idea that you don't trust anybody *under* thirty doesn't emerge.

The moderator: Let me just make that comment over the speaker, for the people in the back, an important point, sometimes overlooked in this controversy. One of the audience expressed the hope that as the reaction to "You can't trust anyone over thirty," there wouldn't develop a backlash movement that would be expressed "You can't trust anybody under thirty."

Same member of the audience: I was prompted to say that

when you said that you can't prove to us that you're not taking it just for kicks. This discussion is supposed to be about LSD in society, and the legal justification for regulating the drugs seems to be based on a pleasure-to-risk ratio, which was unfortunately demonstrated today, what you call a high risk. But nobody has talked about the other thing that you should substitute for pleasure—although pleasure may be applicable in a majority of the cases—the utility-to-risk ratio. Nobody has investigated the fantastic possibilities that LSD brings out, so that the utility could be very, very high, which would balance off, to some extent, the risks. And there's one other orientation in this symposium that bothers me, which I think bothered the writer of the recent letter in our college paper, which is the very scientific cast of the symposium speakers. And I would be the last one to go against science, because it's proved to be very, very successful; but it is strange that there are no artists involved in this, no philosophers, no theologians.

The moderator: Dr. Pahnke does have a degree in religion, I am informed.

Same member of the audience: All right, but at least, say, somebody artistic, who would use this in support of his art. This hasn't really been brought out. Mr. Barron said that the response to this explosion of knowledge and ideas prompts the response —and McLuhan might be relevant here—to try other types of integrating knowledge and intellect in these things. I think LSD might be useful in exploring these areas. This has not been brought out, though it goes right to the thing of the tremendous utility of LSD. So I was wondering if the government and Dr. Louria had considered the possible utility that might balance off some of the risk? Maybe this isn't a very practical question either, as we know that there are a lot of artists who are racked by opium and other drugs who do produce very profound and good poetry. You know, it's hard to tell whether it is worth it or not. But there are laws restricting the use of LSD, and we could be losing a lot. I don't think that this problem has been addressed.

The moderator: The member of the audience has asked if we have paid enough attention to the possibility that LSD has a high utility, which, if legislated against, would be lost to the culture.

Mr. Chayet: On the question of utility and risk, I think that this is a very realistic suggestion, and I would like to say that the law of the country is based very much on utility and risk. What the Supreme Court of the United States says in its earth-shaking decisions, which are often five to four—five jurists thinking one way and four equally learned jurists thinking the other way—is based on a careful balancing of what they think is useful and what they think is the social necessity. The example was brought up today of the automobile—there's a terrific amount of carnage, but we allow it; we don't outlaw it, because of its utility. Now everybody who drives an automobile gets somewhere, and if you could show me that everybody who takes LSD gets somewhere that is useful in a constructive sense, then I would say let's get rid of the laws. Let's allow it. But if you have one person who takes it and really gets somewhere and many hundreds who get nowhere and who go out windows, then I say there's a real question. While I think that your suggestion is a good one, I just don't think that we have reached the point where there is the utility-to-risk ratio that would allow change in legislation.

Member of the audience: You were all here when Dr. Kurland read his case studies, and you also heard Dr. Pahnke's case studies. It seems to me that one thing that all these people had in common—and they admitted it—was that they were all dead before they took the drug, dead in some sense. These drugs were given to somebody—that twenty-three-year-old girl with the illegitimate child, the Negro who was a drinker—and gave them something very real. And this, this introducing of pleasure, just because they and you are supposed to wait for the other— what I really want to say is that it would be a tragedy to wait until seventy years of age, wait fifty years, until science comes up with some kind of result, then take the drugs and find out, by God, I've been missing it all along.

The moderator: As I understand the member of the audience, he has suggested that the protocols presented from the patients indicated a gain in personal phenomenological experience, and the member of the audience felt that if one waited until he was a seventy-year-old person without having had those experiences, it would be a great loss. I shall ask Dr. Kurland to speak to this, if he will.

Dr. Kurland: The issue here is one of—one of the issues, anyway, is, in plain English, impatience. Nobody will realize the impatience and frustrations of the researchers who are actively involved in something like this, who see all the possibilities, yet are aware that society demands that they be responsible to the public trust. Many times we have the very, very frustrating business of going into our proposals and looking for advance research, and then having our peers turn the proposals down, because they say that there is something missing in the specifications, that is, the plans are not well done. So we go back to the drawing board again and again. We don't get everything we ask for. One of the things that we have learned is that our peers sitting in the committees that make judgements have not been wrong most of the time. Most of the time we've been wrong if they haven't approved of something. We have gone back and redesigned our plans so that they can meet the objections, and we have been able to go ahead. For example, when you are dealing with human life and have the responsibility of working in an unknown area, you have to take every precaution to make sure that you are doing everything to make things work out properly. We feel that it is the most important rule in these areas to document what we are doing, so that the way will be clear for the next men to follow through. If our research can't be replicated in Russia or in Australia or in South America, it means that we have not done the job right. We see things in our work that we would like to measure. What we realize is that it may take six months or a year to set up a program so it can be done with safety and consideration for all the elements involved. You can't rush good research. Good research takes a long time, and that is why there are few places that we are able to get the kind of balance needed. For example, with alcoholics, we started in 1960, really 1958, and began following these people. So, we had opportunities of comparing and maintaining balance. But in a behavioral science, when one works with men, when one deals with such complex issues, when one is taking psychotherapy and adding research to it—and you heard how complex this job is—to try to accomplish something, it is frustrating that some feel that they can rush in and get the answers. Maybe we'll have perfected techniques in ten, twenty, thirty years from now.

We have computers today, which we didn't have several years ago, and some of our present experiments are not even possible without computers.

Dr. Pahnke: I detect in both the last two questions a feeling that the panel here has not really taken seriously the possibilities of the drugs, positive possibilities for enriching lives. Such was not the intent of my remarks. I take these possibilities very seriously. I think that there is promise in the experiments, but I do not think that we know enough yet to make statements. We need more research in these very areas, research to determine the utility, but such research and planning for it will take time.

Member of the audience: Generally, I think, everyone here would really have to agree with Dr. Louria's position that scientists are trying to help in understanding these problems as well as in control and prevention of abuse. But let me suggest two other complications; and maybe Dr. Louria or someone on the panel will comment on these. One is that people are obviously continuing to use LSD, the so-called lay people, some of whom do know how to use this drug and have knowledge of therapy. It seems to be a fact. Why do people do this as often as they do? I think that there must be some utility here, and it just can't be dismissed out of hand if enough people are taking it. Too, I think that Dr. Louria's position on the measures that need to be taken to control this drug in the colleges could produce a number of problems that might, in themselves, prove worse than the problem of cure. Fortunately, there are times when the government gets itself into a position of not being able to take a really utilitarian stand and say that the law should stop this problem. We all know that this law will create an environment in which these other probabilities exist. And so we should not permit this law to stand, in order to avoid creating this evil environment. The evidence of heroin abuse suggests that there was a bad environment, which might serve as an example, a situation where there is a black market, and people in the underworld make a fortune on it by smuggling heroin and starting people off on a terrible habit. So that has to be considered. I mean, if you look at this and you look at the answers that a lot of people are giving to these questions, you realize that youth is a bit distrustful. I don't think that there is a really considered opinion that exists in, let's say, the visional people nowadays, which allows the use of LSD some respectability, or in their criticism of existing statutes about the use of LSD.

The moderator: I think that your comments could be summed up as a plea for more open-mindedness in enacting legislation and in implementing programs. I'm not a member of the medical profession, but I think I can say a word or two that will perhaps help you in understanding the feeling of the medical profession about things like this.

There was once a motion picture in which a man fought against a dictator in one of the Latin American countries. He fought, and he fought, and he did everything that he could to reject the concept of help from the establisment, so to speak. Then, accidentally, he became the dictator himself and immediately found himself in political trouble. In what was probably the best punch-line in the movie, he turns to the cabinet of men whom he has been rejecting and says "Help me! Help me!"

I think that that is the feeling that the medical profession has, for in its clinical work they regularly see people who are appealing to them, and they constantly have a feeling of helplessness in the face of certain of these problems. Therefore, their focus tends toward avoidance of these terribly painful situations in which they have to deal somehow with situations that they don't understand, nor know what to do about. And I think that you see strength of expression and a focussing on the negative side.

Dr. Kurland: Actually, there are several issues involved here. One is that it isn't too difficult to do research in this area if you submit a protocol. It's first a question of submitting an experimental design that will be accepted; and the other issue is that of financing. Many studies are accepted, but there just aren't funds available to carry them out. For example, we had the experience of this dying-patient study, which had earlier been submitted on two occasions, and it had been rejected on two occasions. If you have studies that you want to pursue, I'm pretty sure that if they meet the judgement of your scientific peers, they will be approved. Whether it will be funded is another matter, because there are priorities in these matters. One must be aware that there are only certain amounts of money available to go into programs. We have heard that the funds for LSD research have been decreasing for various reasons, which may not be relevant to the research program itself, but to other factors that have no relationship to these programs. If you're really interested in something and go to the extent of submitting it to a scientific body for approval, and if they reject it, there are most probably deficiencies in that design that should be corrected. This has been our experience. Not everything that we submit is approved. Some are rejected, and we go back to try to work them out. And things that are called to our attention are rejected. Sometimes we realize that we were biased in a certain way and that this was a good decision. In the LSD area, despite all the restrictions, you still can do research if you are willing to undertake the effort to have your plan approved. As you heard, the members of the panel are attempting now to work this thing out. There's a very complex administrative procedure because of the unique situation with this compound. When several agencies are involved, it becomes a very complicated manoeuver. Most of the time the rejected designs were rejected because there was a *lack* of some kind in them.

9   The Pharmacology of LSD

By Nicholas J. Giarman

INTRODUCTION

Lysergic acid diethylamide (LSD) is a member of a growing class of drugs, the psychotropic drugs, which are capable of altering, among other things, mood, affect, perception and behavior in man. One must emphasize the phrase "among other things," because no drug can be limited to effects on psychological modalities alone. Other pharmacological actions may be as characteristic of the drug as its psychopharmacological action; so one learns to expect a constellation of somatomotor and autonomic effects as part of the general pharmacology of psychotropic drugs.

Among the psychotropic drugs LSD might be subclassified as a representative of the psychotomimetic agents, *i.e.,* those that produce temporary altered states of thinking and perception in man. This generic grouping of drugs like LSD, mescaline, psilocybin, dimethyltryptamine, *etc.,* while useful for purposes of classification, is not defined by a typical array of pharmacological and behavioral effects in animals (Giarman and Freedman, 1965). It is, rather, defined by behavioral effects in man. In this sense, the pharmacology of LSD is important and unique in many aspects. Its pharmacology is particularly deserving of scrutiny in the face of the current impact of the drug upon society. No drug has probably ever had such profound social repercussions in the brief period of twenty years. After all, it took some centuries for heroin and alcohol to make a similar impact.

CHEMISTRY

LSD is a semi-synthetic compound, the lysergic acid portion of which is a natural product of the ergot fungus *Claviceps purpurea,* which grows on rye and other grains and on certain higher plants. The diethylamide is related structurally to the medically useful uterine stimulant ergonovine, which is an isopropanol amide (Fig. 1).

Inherent in the molecule of LSD is an indole nucleus separated from a nitrogen by two carbon atoms, an arrangement reminiscent of a number of simpler psychotomimetic drugs, such as psilocybin and dimethyltryptamine, as well as of the complex molecule yohimbine, which is not psychotomimetic in man, but appears to create a quite intense and specific "anxiety" (Holmberg and Gershon, 1961). All these compounds bear a structural similarity to the naturally occurring brain neurohumor serotonin, which in

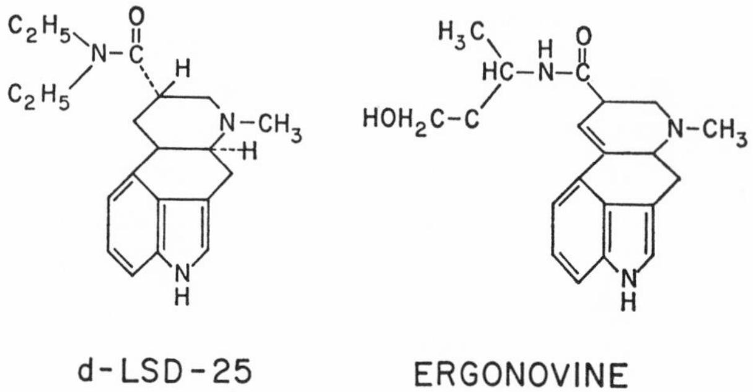

d-LSD-25   ERGONOVINE

Fig. 1. A comparison of the chemical structures of LSD and ergonovine.

itself is not psychotomimetic, but which has been implicated in a number of heuristic hypotheses linking brain function to its biochemistry (Fig. 2).

Another important aspect of the chemistry of LSD is the stereospecificity of action. There is an iso-LSD as well as the LSD molecule, each of which is optically active. Of the resulting four stereoisomers only one, dextro-rotatory LSD, is pharmacologically active. This would indicate a high selectivity at the site of action of LSD in the brain.

Finally, among the substitutions on the amide grouping, only the mono-ethyl (LAE) and the di-ethyl (LSD) possess psychogenic activity; the mono-methyl, di-methyl, propyl and butyl derivatives are without activity. The acetylated derivative of LSD (ALD) and 1-methyl-LSD (MLD) retain psychotomimetic activity (Fig. 3).

GENERAL PHARMACOLOGICAL ACTIVITY

The pharmacology of LSD is summarized in Fig. 4, taken from a review by Rothlin (Rothlin, 1957). It is clear that in addition to central actions on psychic functions, there are also effects upon

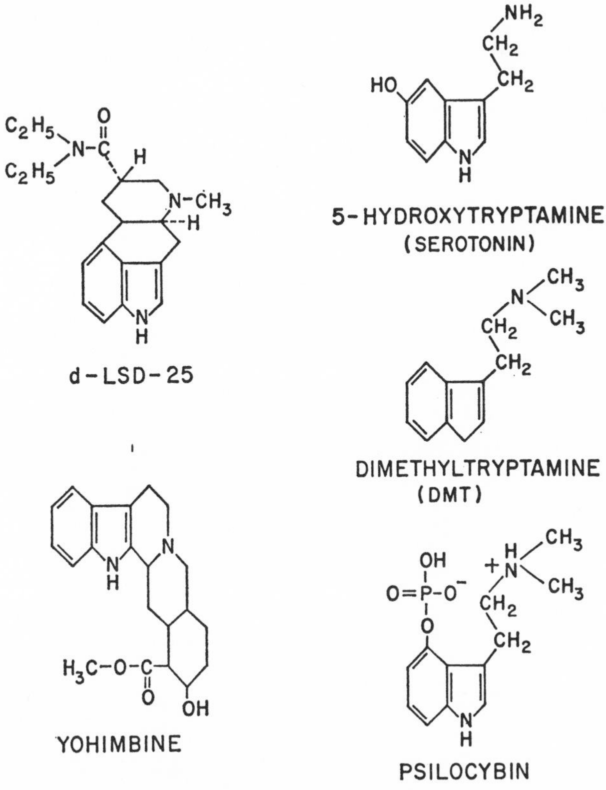

Fig. 2. The structural formulae of certain psychoactive drugs similar to LSD and their similarity to the structure of 5-hydroxytryptamine (serotonin).

somatomotor functions and upon functions subserved by the autonomic nervous system. These latter include both sympathomimetic and parasympathomimetic actions, which are of central origin, since they are absent in the spinal cat and are blocked by peripherally acting ganglion-blocking and neuro-effector-blocking

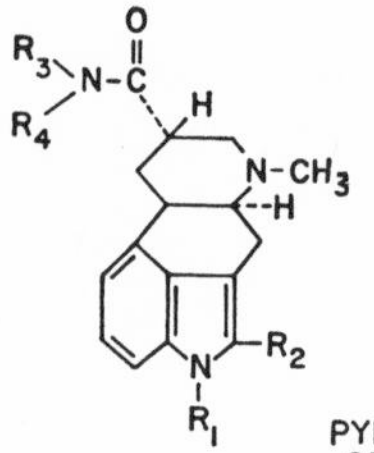

COMPOUND	R_1	R_2	R_3	R_4	PYRETO-GENIC ACTION	PSYCHOTO-MIMETIC EFFECT	SEROTONIN ANTAGONISM
LSD-25	-H	-H	$-C_2H_5$	$-C_2H_5$	100	100	100
ALD-52	$-COCH_3$	-H	$-C_2H_5$	$-C_2H_5$	13	100	200
BOL-148	-H	-Br	$-C_2H_5$	$-C_2H_5$	5	0	103
MLD-41	$-CH_3$	-H	$-C_2H_5$	$-C_2H_5$	5	40	370
UML-491	$-CH_3$	-H	-H	$-CH\genfrac{}{}{0pt}{}{C_2H_5}{CHOH}$		0	400

Fig. 3. The relationship of the chemical structure of LSD and some congeners to certain pharmacological actions.

CENTRAL ACTIONS UPON:

Psychic functions	*Somatomotor functions*	*Autonomic nervous functions*
Excitation	Pyramidal and extrapy-	(a) Meso-diencephalic
Mood changes: euphoria	ramidal effects: ataxia	effects
depression	and spastic paralysis	Mydriasis
Disturbances of perception		Tachycardia
Hallucinations		Rise in body temper-
Depersonalisation		ature
Psychotic states		Hyperglycemia
		Pilomotor reaction
		(b) Medullary or bulbar
		effects:
		Lowering of blood
		pressure
		Bradycardia
		Respiratory depression

LSD
Diethylamide of
(+)-lysergic acid

DIRECT PERIPHERAL ACTIONS UPON:

Constriction of:
Uterus *in vitro* and *vivo*
Blood vessels artificially perfused
Bronchial musculature in high doses
Blood vessels of spinal cat
Adrenolytic action on isolated uterus and seminal vesicle
Inhibition of 5-HT on different organs *in vitro* and *in vivo*

Fig. 4. A summary of the general pharmacology of LSD. Reproduced by permission from Rothlin, 1957.

agents. While many of these effects may be seen in the same individual of a given species, some differences in autonomic effects will arise. There are, of course, individual and species differences (*e.g.,* the rabbit is extremely sensitive to the hyperthermic effects of LSD); in addition, there are differences due to such factors as dose (*e.g.,* respiratory depression is seen only in toxic doses) and anaesthesia.

Apart from these centrally mediated actions, the drug has a variety of direct effects upon certain peripheral structures, such as the uterus and the blood-vessels, leading to contraction of smooth muscle in these organs.

DOMINANT PHARMACOLOGICAL CHARACTERISTICS

1. *Serotonin antagonism.* One of the unique pharmacological characteristics of LSD is the fact that in peripheral organs stimulated by 5-hydroxytryptamine (serotonin, 5-HT) LSD is a powerful antagonist of the amine and can also mimic its action. This antagonism was discovered by Gaddum (Gaddum and Hameed, 1954) and can be demonstrated on the smooth muscle of a number of organs as well as on certain structures of invertebrates, *e.g.,* the heart of *Venus mercenaria.* LSD has a remarkable potency in this regard. For example, it inhibits the 5-HT-induced contractile response of the rat uterus in a concentration of 1 mμg/ml (10^{-9} gm), and the effect persists for 90 minutes (Lanz, Cerletti and Rothlin, 1955). Even more striking is the report of Welch (Welch, 1954) that LSD in concentrations of 10^{-18} gm *potentiates* the contractile response of the clam heart to 10^{-9} gm of 5-HT. This is an illustration of the partial agonist nature of LSD, *i.e.,* the mimicking of 5-HT action before the blocking effect is observed. This dual effect of LSD is observable in other isolated organ systems, such as the isolated rat uterus.

2. *Potency.* Perhaps one of the most striking pharmacological characteristics of LSD is its potency. While there is a species difference in sensitivity to the behavioral effects of LSD, the effective oral dose in normal human beings is as small as 0.5 to 1 μg/kg, which makes LSD 3000 to 5000 times more potent than mescaline in producing similar psychic changes. Although as much as 2 to 2.5 μg/kg are sometimes taken by human beings, the amounts that are found in brain represent at most only 1% of the

dose taken. This impressive fact points to extreme sensitivity of some critical brain receptors for the drug.

3. *Absorption, distribution, metabolism and excretion.* It is common knowledge that LSD is well absorbed from the gastro-intestinal mucosa after oral administration, and it is rarely administered by any other route. Studies in the cat show that even though considerable amounts of LSD become bound to blood protein, the drug is, nevertheless, rapidly distributed to the body tissues, the

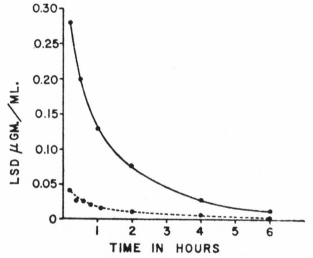

Fig. 5. The rate of clearance of LSD from blood (solid line) and cerebrospinal fluid (broken line) of the monkey after a dose of 200 μg/kg administered intravenously. Reproduced by permission from Axelrod *et al.*, 1957.

highest concentrations appearing in the lung, liver, kidney and brain (Axelrod, Brady, Witkop and Evarts, 1957).

A very high proportion of the dose is found in the bile, which is probably the preferred route of excretion. One of the inactive excretion products is 2-oxy-LSD, which is formed in liver microsomes by an NADH-dependent enzyme (Axelrod *et al.*, 1957). In addition, Boyd (Boyd, 1959) has reported the presence of two metabolites in rat bile after C^{14}-LSD, which are suggested to be the β-glucuronides of hydroxy-LSD and hydroxy-iso-LSD. Szara (Szara, 1963) has also indicated the formation of hydroxylated LSD, probably in the 13-position, by rat and guinea-pig liver.

Whether hydroxy-LSD is psychotomimetic in man has not been determined.

Exclusive of protein binding, LSD seems to be distributed throughout the body water with little impedance by anatomic barriers. Figure 5 (Axelrod *et al.,* 1957) shows the rate of clearance of LSD from the blood and cerebrospinal fluid (CSF) of the monkey after 200 μg/kg given intravenously. Since the amount of drug present in the cerebrospinal fluid was about the same as the

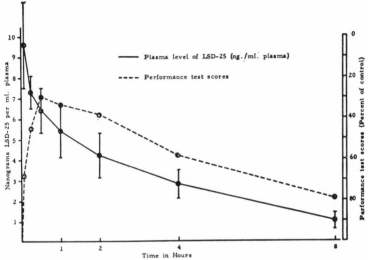

Fig. 6. The mean plasma levels of LSD in man after a dose of 2 μg/kg administered intravenously are expressed as ng/ml of plasma and appear on the scale at the left. The standard deviation for each value is indicated. The mean-performance test scores, expressed as a percentage of control scores, appear on the scale at the right. Reproduced by permission from Aghajanian and Bing, 1964.

unbound amount in the plasma, it has been concluded that there is little hindrance to the passage of "free" LSD across the blood-brain barrier. The biologic half-life, which is a measure of the rate of metabolism of the drug and its sojourn in the blood, has been calculated to be 100 minutes in the monkey, 130 minutes in the cat and 7 minutes in the mouse. Such variation has prompted Aghajanian and Bing to warn that it is hazardous to apply data on LSD from a particular animal species to man (Aghajanian and Bing, 1964). In the only investigation of levels of LSD in the blood of human beings, these investigators have shown (Fig. 6) that reasonably high levels of LSD (relative to the dose of 2 μg/kg) are achieved in human plasma after intravenous administration; and, what is more important, there seems to be a close relationship between the presence of LSD and effects on the brain, demonstrated in this case by ability to perform a simple arithmetic test (Aghajanian and Bing, 1964). Assuming that presence of the drug in blood is a reflection of its presence in brain, these results do not support earlier hypotheses that LSD "triggers" a reaction that outlasts the drug's stay in the body, hypotheses that were based

TABLE I

Comparison of LSD Content of Various Regions of Monkey Brain
Reprinted by permission from Snyder and Reivich, 1966.

	Ratio to frontal gray concentration*	p value
Superficial cerebral structures	1.12 ± 0.03	—
Extrapyramidal system	1.69 ± 0.09†	< 0.001
Visual and auditory reflex areas	3.37 ± 0.26†	< 0.001
Hypothalamus	2.96 ± 0.06†	< 0.001
Thalamus	1.46 ± 0.10†	< 0.05
Limbic system	2.74 ± 0.15†	< 0.001
Pituitary gland	8.05 ± 1.75†	< 0.02
Pineal gland	6.85 ± 0.71†	0.005
Cerebellum	0.81 ± 0.09†	< 0.02
Brain stem	1.09 ± 0.19	< 0.8

  * Mean ± S.E.M.

  † Significantly different from superficial cerebral structures (Student's *t* test)

upon the short half-life in mouse blood and brain (Haley and Rutschmann, 1957; Osmond, 1957; Unger, 1963). Aghajanian and Bing calculated a half-life of 175 minutes for LSD in man (Aghajanian and Bing, 1964).

With any psychotropic drug it is obviously of interest to determine whether the drug tends to localize in any specific region of the brain. Snyder and Reivich have examined this problem in the monkey (Snyder and Reivich, 1966). Some of their results, shown in Table I, indicate that the highest amounts of LSD after intravenous administration are found in the pituitary and pineal glands. Other regions of particular concentration over the amount in the cortex were structures of the limbic system (hippocampus, amygdala, fornix and septal region) and, to some extent, the

thalamus and hypothalamus. This accumulation of LSD in mesen-
cephalic and diencephalic structures, associated with autonomic
centers in the brain, correlates well with the centrally mediated
autonomic effects of the drug. In view of effects of LSD on visual

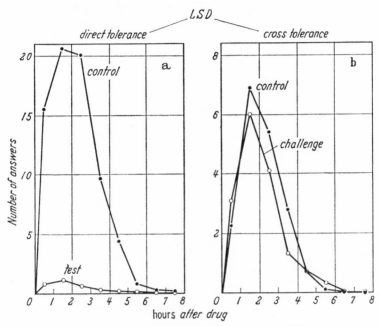

Fig. 7. Time course of the subjective response to LSD before (•)
and after (○) the chronic administration of LSD (section *a* on the
left) and after the chronic administration of D-amphetamine (section
b on the right). Note in section *a* the marked diminution in response
to LSD, 1.5 μg/kg after chronic LSD administration, *i.e.,* direct
tolerance is present; but in section *b,* the normal response to LSD,
0.5 μg/kg after chronic D-amphetamine administration, *i.e.,* cross-
tolerance is absent. Reproduced by permission from Rosenberg *et al.,*
1963.

mechanisms, it was of interest to find that the drug was not concentrated in the visual cortex, as it was in the deep visual reflex
centers (such as lateral and medial geniculate bodies and the
optic chiasm). By way of comparison Neff *et al.* (Neff, Rossi, Chase
and Rabinowitz, 1964) found that mescaline, like LSD, was
present in high concentration in the pituitary gland and in the
lateral and medial geniculate bodies.

4. *Tolerance and cross-tolerance.* Another striking feature in the pharmacology of LSD is the rapid development of tolerance, so that after a few days of repeated use a previously effective dose no longer produces a response. This phenomenon is observable in studies of the behavioral effects of the drug in either man or animals (Fig. 7: Rosenberg, Wolback, Miner and Isbell, 1963). It is clear that cross tolerance with dextro-amphetamine does not

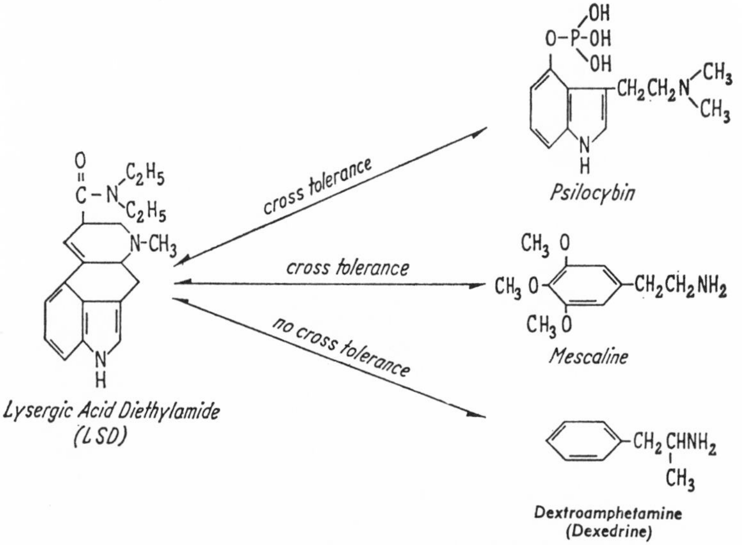

Fig. 8. Cross-tolerance and structural relationships among LSD, psilocybin, mescaline and D-amphetamine. Reproduced by permission from Rosenberg *et al.,* 1963.

exist; however, further studies by Rosenberg *et al.* (Rosenberg *et al.,* 1963) did establish a remarkable cross-tolerance between LSD and psilocybin and between LSD and mescaline (Fig. 8). This need not indicate that these three psychotomimetic agents affect the same receptors in the brain; and, if this is not so, it might indicate that each drug engages a chain of reactions that merge to a final common pathway. It is of interest that along with the behavioral effects, certain centrally mediated effects of LSD, such as pyrexia, EEG-alerting and mydriasis show tolerance, but salivation and brachycardia do not (Giarman and Friedman, 1965).

HYPOTHESES OF THE MECHANISM OF ACTION OF LSD

Two types of hypotheses of the mechanism of action of LSD have been proposed: the neurophysiological, which is beyond the scope of this paper, and the neurochemical. The first neurochemical theory of LSD's mechanism arose from the well documented antagonism between LSD and 5-HT in peripheral structures. Such and interrelationship was attractive, because 5-HT is considered to play some as yet undefined neurophysiological role. As mentioned above, small quantities of LSD were known to imitate effects of 5-HT, while larger amounts demonstrated the antagonism. It was, therefore, speculated that excesses or deficiencies of 5-HT at critical receptor sites might govern normal or abnormal mental function (Gaddum, 1957; Woolley and Shaw, 1957). When other analogues of LSD were tested, however, it became clear that psychotomimetic action could not be correlated with peripheral 5-HT antagonism (Fig. 3).

A link with 5-HT metabolism in brain could not be ruled out, however, when Freedman and Giarman first showed that LSD caused in the rat brain a small (20%), but reproducible increase in the level of 5-HT, all of which could be accounted for in particle-bound 5-HT (Table II: Freedman, 1961; Freedman and Giarman, 1962). It is clear from these data that the effects of LSD are quite the opposite to those produced by reserpine. It is also of interest that while 5-hydroxytryptophan increases the total 5-HT, it actually decreases the percentage that is "bound." Brom-LSD, which has little behavioral effect, did not influence 5-HT levels, but psychoactive congeners (LAE and MLD) did (Freedman, 1963). More recently, Freedman and co-workers have found that as the 5-HT is increased and bound in the brain after LSD, the metabolic end-product of 5-HT, 5-hydroxy-indoleacetic acid, is concomitantly decreased (Fig. 9: Freedman, Lovell and Rosecrans, to be published). This is precisely what one would expect under conditions of increased binding of 5-HT. Another interesting aspect of this relationship is that the increase in brain 5-HT appears 15 to 30 minutes after the administration of LSD, which correlates roughly with the termination of the acute behavioral effect (40 minutes in the rat), and disappears in about four hours, when all drug effects are gone. Thus the uptake and clearance of LSD by

TABLE II

Subcellular Distribution of Serotonin (5-HT) in the Rat Brain and Changes Produced by Certain Chemical Agents
Adapted from Giarman, Freedman and Schanberg, 1964.

Treatment	Number of animals	Mean level of 5-HT (mμg/brain) in				p^*
		Total	Partic.** ("bound")	Supernatant ("free")	% of Total "bound"	
None	150	649	498	151	77	—
Reserpine (5 μg/kg, 24 h)	18	170	112	58	66	< 0.01
LSD-25 (1.3 μg/kg, 40 min)	12	752	623	129	83	< 0.001
5-Hydroxytryptophan (100 μg/kg, 20 min)	18	1090	760	330	70	< 0.01

* Represents level of significance of difference from control, calculated by means of Student's *t* test.
** Particulate fraction after centrifugation for 2×10^6 g min.

brain are critically related to the effects noted on levels and sub-cellular distribution of 5-HT. During the period of change in 5-HT levels, there is also a *decrease* in the levels of another brain neurohumor, norepinephrine, which is thought to be related to the excitation produced by LSD (Freedman and Aghajanian, 1966).

Finally, the relationship between LSD and these brain amines

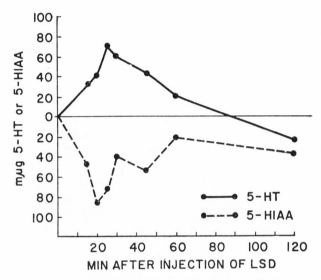

Fig. 9. The response of brain levels of 5-HT (solid line) and 5-hydroxyindole acetic acid (5-HIAA, broken line) in the rat after administration of LSD. Reproduced by permission from Freedman, Lovell and Rosecrans, to be published.

becomes more significant with the finding that if one alters the metabolism of the amines prior to the administration of LSD, there is a marked change in the intensity of the effects of LSD on the brain. For example, when brain monoamines are depleted by reserpine, the behavioral effects of LSD are notably enhanced and prolonged in both rat and man (Appel and Freedman, 1964; Resnick, Krus and Raskin, 1965). Conversely, when the biogenic amines in brain are elevated by pretreatment with an in-hibitor of monoamine oxidase, the enzyme that destroys the amines, the behavioral effects of LSD in man are markedly diminished (Resnick, Krus and Raskin, 1964). Freedman and

Aghajanian (Freedman and Aghajanian, 1966) have speculated about the interaction between LSD and biogenic amines in this manner: "The amines normally may have a silent 'buffering' function with respect to certain dimensions of intensity in behavior, and by a change in the regulation of their life cycle it is possible that this normal function becomes unmasked." This concept is in keeping with many of the known peripheral effects of 5-HT related to sensitization of a number of receptors, *e.g.*, 5-HT sensitizes pain receptors in the skin, baroreceptors in the lung, pressure receptors in the gastro-intestinal mucosa and chemoreceptors in the carotid body.

TOXICITY*

Except for the rabbit, which is extraordinarily sensitive to LSD, the acute toxicity of this drug is not considered remarkably high. Acute LSD poisoning is devoid of any specific features, but death in all species results from respiratory failure. There are no reports of death in man due to the *direct toxic action* of the drug.

In man, however, the toxicity of LSD has some especial implications. Contrary to some statements in the literature, serious complications arising from the administration of LSD to man can no longer be considered infrequent. The clearest danger from the use of LSD-type drugs is to borderline psychotic and depressed patients. Several warnings have been issued (Cohen and Ditman, 1963; Cole and Katz, 1964; Fink, Simeon, Hague and Itil, 1966). Severe reactions in man to LSD may be classified into three groups: (1) acute reactions; (2) recurrent reactions; and (3) prolonged effects.

The acute reactions are of two types: a toxic state of acute paranoia and confusion, which can lead to dangerous behavior and suicide; and a panic state, which is probably not a direct toxic

---

* Since this manuscript was submitted for publication, there has been published a report that indicates a new and unexpected type of toxicity produced by LSD in human beings (Irwin, S., and Egozcue, J.: Chromosomal abnormalities in leukocytes from LSD-25 users. *Science*, 1967, *157*: 313-314). This took the form of a significant increase in chromosomal abnormalities in the leukocytes of six out of eight LSD-25 users, compared to one out of nine non-users as controls. The authors admit that it is too early to assess the significance of these findings, but one cannot deny that this represents an unanticipated potential danger of LSD to man.

effect of the drug, but rather the patient's reaction to the drug state. Recurrent reactions have been seen in patients up to one year after the last use of the drug. The prolonged effects consist of chronic anxiety states with preponderance of visual phenomena and depersonalization. These effects may last many months and are resistant to pharmacotherapy and psychotherapy. Thus the hazard of LSD administration appears to lie in the decrease of affective and emotional controls and in the induction of a persistent state of altered thinking and perception.

In summary, LSD is a psychotropic drug with several unique pharmacological characteristics. Indirect and circumstantial evidence is available to link the brain effects of LSD to central systems regulating the disposition of 5-HT and possibly norepinephrine. The toxic potential of LSD in man is not insignificant.

REFERENCES

Aghajanian, G. K., and Bing, O. H. L. Persistence of lysergic acid diethylamide in the plasma of human subjects. *Clin. Pharm. and Ther.*, 1964, *5:* 611.

Appel, J. B., and Freedman, D. X. Chemically-induced alterations in the behavioral effects of LSD-25. *Biochem. Pharmacol.*, 1964, *13:* 861.

Axelrod, J., Brady, R. O., Witkop, B., and Evarts, E. V. The distribution and metabolism of lysergic acid diethylamide. *Ann. N. Y. Acad. Sci.*, 1957, *66:* 435.

Boyd, E. S. The metabolism of lysergic acid diethylamide. *Arch. int. Pharmacodyn.*, 1959, *120:* 292.

Cohen, S., and Ditman, K. S. Prolonged adverse reactions to lysergic acid diethylamide. *Arch. Gen. Psychiat.*, 1963, *8:* 475.

Cole, J. O., and Katz, M. M. The psychotomimetic drugs. *J. A. M. A.*, 1964, *187:* 758.

Fink, M., Simeon, J., Hague, W., and Itil, T. Prolonged adverse reactions to LSD in psychotic subjects. *Arch. Gen. Psychiat.*, 1966, *15:* 450.

Freedman, D. X. Effects of LSD-25 on brain serotonin. *J. Pharmacol. Exper. Therap.*, 1961, *134:* 160.

Freedman, D. X. Psychotomimetic drugs and brain biogenic amines. *Am. J. Psychiat.*, 1963, *119:* 843.

Freedman, D. X., and Aghajanian, G. K. Approaches to the pharmacology of LSD-25. *Lloydia*, 1966, *29:* 309.

Freedman, D. X., and Giarman, N. J. LSD-25 and the status and level of brain serotonin. *Ann. N. Y. Acad. Sci.*, 1962, *96:* 98.

Freedman, D. X., Lovell, R. A., and Rosecrans, J. A. In personal communication about work to be published.

Gaddum, J. H.: Serotonin-LSD interactions. *Ann. N. Y. Acad. Sci.,* 1957, *66:* 643.

Gaddum, J. H., and Hameed, K. A. Drugs which antagonize 5-hydroxy-tryptamine. *Brit. J. Pharmacol.,* 1954, *9:* 240.

Giarman, N. J., and Freedman, D. X. Biochemical aspects of psychotomimetic drug action. *Pharmacol. Rev.,* 1965, *17:* 1.

Giarman, N. J., Freedman, D. X., and Schanberg, S. M. Drug-induced changes in the subcellular distribution of serotonin in rat brain with special reference to the action of reserpine. In H. E. Himwich and W. A. Himwich (eds.), *Progress in Brain Research, Biogenic Amines.* Amsterdam: Elsevier Publishing Company, 1964, vol. 8, p. 72.

Haley, T. B., and Rutschmann, J.: Brain concentrations of LSD-25 after intracerebral or intravenous administration in conscious animals. *Experientia,* 1957, *13:* 199.

Holmberg, G., and Gershon, S. Autonomic and psychic effects of yohimbine hydrochloride. *Psychopharmacol.,* 1961, *2:* 93.

Lanz, J., Cerletti, A., and Rothlin, E. Über die verteilung des lysergsäurediäthylamids in organismus. *Helv. Physiol. Pharmacol. Acta,* 1955, *13:* 207.

Neff, N., Rossi, G. V., Chase, G. D., and Rabinowitz, J. L. Distribution and metabolism of mescaline-C^{14} in cat brain. *J. Pharmacol.,* 1964, *144:* 1.

Osmond, H. Review of the clinical effects of psychotomimetic agents. *Ann. N. Y. Acad. Sci.,* 1957, *66:* 418.

Resnick, O., Krus, D. M., and Raskin, M. Accentuation of the psychological effects of LSD-25 in normal subjects treated with reserpine. *Life Sci.,* 1965, *4:* 1433.

Resnick, O., Krus, D. M., and Raskin, M. LSD-25 action in normal subjects treated with a monoamine oxidase inhibitor. *Life Sci.,* 1964, *3:* 1207.

Rosenberg, D. E., Wolbach, A. B., Miner, E. J., and Isbell, H. Observations on direct and cross-tolerance with LSD and D-amphetamine in man. *Psychopharmacol.,* 1963, *5:* 1.

Rothlin, E. Pharmacology of lysergic acid diethylamide and some related compounds. *J. Pharm. and Pharmacol.,* 1957, *9:* 569.

Snyder, S. H., and Reivich, M. Regional localization of lysergic acid diethylamide in monkey brain. *Nature,* 1966, *209:* 1093.

Szara, S. Enzymatic formation of a phenolic metabolite from LSD by rat liver microsomes. *Life Sci.,* 1963, *1:* 662.

Unger, S. M. Mescaline, LSD, psilocybin and personality change. *Psychiatry,* 1963, *26:* 111.

Welch, J. H. Marine invertebrate preparations useful in the bioassay of acetylcholine and 5-hydroxytryptamine. *Nature,* 1954, *173:* 955.

Woolley, D. W., and Shaw, E. N. Evidence for the participation of serotonin in mental processes. *Ann. N. Y. Acad. Sci.,* 1957, *66:* 649.

10   Neurophysiological Actions of LSD

By DOMINICK P. PURPURA

INTRODUCTION

ATTEMPTS to define the psychotomimetic effects of LSD in terms
of the properties and behavior of neurons and neuronal organizations have presented a number of challenges to the neurophysiologist, largely as a result of the necessity to examine the actions of
hallucinogenic drugs on neuronal systems whose normal operations
are incompletely understood. For this reason neurophysiologists
have generally worked with relatively "simple" and well characterized neuronal systems in which a variable degree of control can
be achieved over input and output functions of the system. Although a considerable amount of information has been forthcoming
from such studies in specifying the effects of LSD, the extent to
which the data obtained can be extrapolated to "behavior" has
been a matter of no little concern. One solution to this problem has
been attempted in the design of experiments in which behavioral
effects of LSD are correlated with changes in one or another variety
of brain-wave activity. But what these studies gain in applicability
to the LSD problem they lose in precision of analysis. For it
has not been possible from available data to relate changes in the
amplitude, frequency or polarity of complex potentials recorded
from different brain structures to the activities of neuronal organizations presumably involved in the production of these wave-forms.
Further complications arise in attempts to assign a unique type of
brain-wave pattern to a particular alteration in behavior. Despite
these obvious problems, several impressive advances have been
made in such analyses as well as in the study of "isolated" neuronal
systems.

   This survey is concerned with several types of studies that have
provided important clues to the mode of action of LSD on neuronal
organizations of varying complexity. Since no exhaustive treatment

of the several hundred reports on this subject is possible, the studies selected for examination will obviously reflect the author's bias in regard to the possible mechanisms of LSD action and in the identification of brain structures in which LSD effects are likely to produce dramatic alterations in behavior. A few introductory remarks concerning the general types of neurophysiological activities examined here will be useful.

THE ELECTRICAL ACTIVITY OF NEURONS AND THE ORIGIN AND NATURE OF BRAIN WAVES

Neurons in the mammalian brain differ widely in size, length and number of dendrites and in length and distribution of axons. Depending upon the criteria for defining cell types, it is possible to identify several hundred morphologically different neurons in the central nervous system (Ramón y Cajal, 1909). From a physiological standpoint neurons are either excitatory or inhibitory in the effects that they produce upon one another. Such effects are mediated at specialized junctions or synapses between the axon of one neuron and the cell body and/or dendrites of another (Eccles, 1964). Excitation from one neuron to another occurs when an all-or-none response or action potential propagates into the axon-terminal. Depolarization of the terminal triggers the release of a chemical transmitter agent that diffuses across the 200-ångstra space between the axon-terminal (presynaptic element) and the cell body or dendrite of the postsynaptic element and activates a specialized portion (receptor patch) of the postsynaptic membrane (Grundfest, 1966). The interaction of the transmitter agent and the receptor patch on the postsynaptic membrane probably induces a specific conformational change in the complex lipoproteins that constitute the neuron membrane. As a consequence of this the membrane permeability for sodium and potassium ions is increased. The movement of these cations down their electrochemical gradients initiates local currents that produce a graded membrane depolarization, the excitatory postsynaptic potential (EPSP). The amplitude and time course of the EPSP is determined by the duration of transmitter action, number of synaptic sites activated and certain properties of the postsynaptic cell membrane (Eccles, 1964). If the depolarizing potential generated at excitatory synapses reaches a critical magnitude, a sequence of permeability changes to sodium and potassium ions is initiated in membrane sites adjacent to the subsynaptic receptor patches. These permeability changes produce ionic currents reflected in an all-or-none, propagating-action potential. Impulses may recur many hundreds of times per second depending on the nature and magnitude of the excitatory synaptic drive and the properties of the axon and cell body in which the spike potentials are generated.

Excitatory neurons differ physiologically from inhibitory neurons in the nature of the permeability change induced in the postsynaptic membrane by the transmitter agents released from their axon-terminals. An excitatory transmitter produces postsynaptic-membrane conductances that lead to depolarization and eventually impulse initiation in the postsynaptic cell. The transmitter released at the nerve terminal of an inhibitory neuron induces a postsynaptic-membrane permeability change largely for chloride ions and to a lesser extent for potassium ions. The currents that flow during the increased permeability to chloride and/or potassium ions tend to hold the membrane potential at a level slightly above the resting value, depending on the type of neuron. In most neurons of the mammalian central nervous system an inhibitory neuron generates a hyperpolarizing, inhibitory postsynaptic potential (IPSP) in the postsynaptic cell. Durations of IPSP's may range from a few to several hundred milliseconds in some central neurons. As in the case of EPSP's, IPSP durations depend upon the duration of inhibitory transmitter actions, spatial and temporal summation of IPSP's and membrane properties of the postsynaptic element.

Each neuron in the brain is covered with thousands of synapses, *i.e.,* the specialized regions of contiguity between the axon-terminal of one neuron and the cell body or dendrites of another. Some neurons such as the Purkinje cells in the cerebellum may have hundreds of thousands of synapses. Synapses on the cell bodies of neurons are referred to as axosomatic synapses; those on the dendritic trunks, dendritic spines or terminal processes are called axodendritic synapses.

The extraordinary advances in recent years in the study of structure and function of synapses are clearly illustrative of the importance placed upon these elements in understanding the functional activity of the brain. The reason for this lies in the fact that the major form of activity involved in the production of brain waves is that which occurs at synapses (Purpura, 1959). It is now possible to state with reasonable assurance that brain waves represent a complex summation of the activities of literally thousands of *excitatory and inhibitory synapses*. All varieties of evoked potentials recorded from the surface or depth of the brain are summations of excitatory and inhibitory postsynaptic potentials generated at the cell bodies and dendrites of neurons in different neuronal organizations. Since the dendrites of most neurons constitute more than 90% of the cell surface available for synaptic contacts, it is proper to speak of brain waves as arising largely from the synaptic events generated in dendrites. Dendrites of most types of neurons in the mammalian brain generate EPSP's and IPSP's, which electrotonically influence sites of impulse initiation in the axon close to the cell body (Eccles, 1957). In some neurons under certain conditions impulse initiation and propagation may occur in dendrites (Purpura, 1967). However, for the most part the somadendritic membrane of central neurons constitutes a synaptic receptor surface, upon which excitatory and inhibitory influences interact in varying proportions. Thus small changes in excitatory or inhibitory synaptic drive may be sufficient to trigger an all-or-none propagating impulse, or conversely to suppress impulse initiation. Since synapses control the excitability of neurons, and since synaptic activities constitute the major neuronal event underlying brain waves, it is understandable that many interpretations of the neurophysiological effects of LSD have focussed on synapses as the primary site of action of LSD.

THE EFFECTS OF LSD ON VISUAL AND AUDITORY PATHWAYS

The prominent visual disturbances produced by LSD in man served as a logical point of departure for several of the earliest neurophysiological studies of LSD and related hallucinogenic agents. It would seem to be a relatively simple matter to determine the nature of the changes produced by LSD at various sites along the visual or auditory projection pathway by appropriate stimulation and registration of evoked electrical activities. Such has not been the case for reasons that are apparent in any evaluation of results obtained from a number of laboratories in which different operational methods are employed in neurophysiological investigations. The problem here is the definition of "experimental design," which involves consideration of the animal species, type and level of anaesthesia (if any), the environmental conditions under which the experiment is carried out, site of stimulation and recording, nature of the electrical activity examined and quantity and mode of administration of the drug. These factors have greatly contributed to the difficulty of obtaining a satisfactory consensus on the mode of action of LSD at any one neuroaxial site.

The effects of anaesthetic agents and other factors in conditioning the overt neurophysiological actions of LSD are well illustrated in the case of studies on the visual system of animals. It is known that a brief intense flash of light will evoke a burst of discharges in the optic nerve, which can be recorded as a summated potential of a population of axons as shown in *Figure 1a*. Very high concentrations of LSD (2.5 mg/kg) administered intravenously produced a marked depression of such photically evoked activity in the optic tract (*Figure 1b*: Evarts, Landau, Freygang and Marshall, 1955). Additional effects were demonstrable when a fine recording electrode was introduced into the lateral geniculate body, the specific thalamic relay nucleus of the visual projection pathway to the cerebral cortex. High-frequency stimulation of the optic nerve in anaesthetized cats resulted in rapid attenuation of the postsynaptic response of lateral geniculate neurons (*Figure 2a*). Following an intracarotid injection of 15 μg/kg of LSD, the first stimulus of the repetitive train to the optic nerve produced a postsynaptic response that was markedly depressed. The depression resembled that produced by repetitive stimulation in the absence of LSD and could be reversed by a brief period of asphyxiation.

Essentially similar results to those described above have been obtained in studies of anaesthetized cats in which comparisons were made between optic nerve potentials, lateral geniculate activity and cortical responses to geniculate stimulation. In these experiments (*Figure 3*) effects of LSD (250 μg) were demonstrable only on the postsynaptic response of the lateral geniculate nucleus, indicating a preferential blocking action of the hallucinogen on the thalamic relay in the visual pathway under the conditions of the study (Bishop, Burke and Hayhow, 1959).

Before considering other aspects of LSD's actions on visually evoked responses of cerebral cortex, it should be noted that several efforts have been made to clarify the possible role of LSD-induced changes in retinal activity. The electroretinogram of the cat exhibits spontaneous activity after LSD (Apter and Pfeiffer, 1960), and this has been confirmed by recording from optic tract and lateral

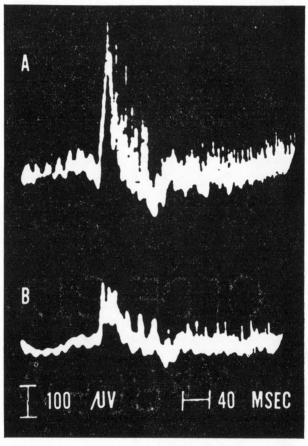

Fig. 1. The effect of LSD on optic-tract responses to retinal photic stimulation of a cat anaesthetized with pentobarbital: *A* before injection, and *B* after injection of 2.5 mg/kg of LSD via the carotid artery. LSD produces a marked depression of the integrated response of optic-tract axons to a single intense light flash. Modified from Evarts *et al.*, 1955.

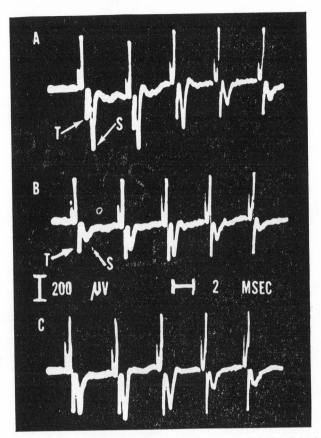

Fig. 2. The effect of LSD on responses recorded in left lateral geniculate body following high-frequency stimulation (250/sec) of optic nerve. *A* before and *B* after 15 µg/kg of LSD via right carotid artery. *T* refers to the optic tract or presynaptic response, and *S* refers to the synchronous postsynaptic component of the lateral geniculate response. Note the depression of first *S* response after LSD and some recovery during early phases of repetitive stimulation. *C* shows recovery from LSD-induced depression by brief (20 sec) period of asphyxiation. The recovery produced by repetitive stimulation and asphyxiation is thought to be reminiscent of the recovery from curare blockade seen at the neuromuscular junction following these procedures. Modified from Evarts *et al.,* 1955.

geniculate body (Schwartz and Cheney, 1965a). The latter studies have been extended to investigations on unanaesthetized cats with chronically implanted electrodes. While it had been shown that low doses of LSD increase spontaneous optic tract discharges, high doses (0.25-1 mg/kg, given intraperitoneally) produced significant depression of such activity in optic tract and lateral geniculate body (*Figure 4*), whether the animals were in the dark or were light-adapted (Schwartz and Cheney, 1965b). It is significant that bilateral section of the optic tract, thereby eliminating any activity originating in centrifugal elements, did not affect the results. It is clear from these studies that LSD has an important action at the

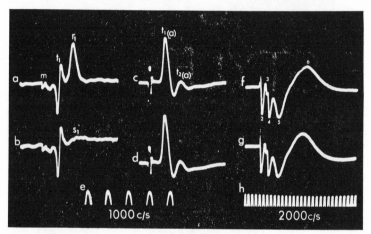

Fig. 3. The effect of LSD on optic tract, geniculate synapses, radiation axons and visual cortex: *a, c* and *f*, before LSD; *b, d* and *g*, after LSD; *a* and *b*, response of geniculate nucleus to stimulation of contralateral optic nerve; *c* and *d*, response of optic nerve to stimulation of optic-tract nerve endings; *f* and *g*, response of visual cortex to stimulation of radiation axons. *a* through *d*, same preparation, 200 μg LSD: *f* and *g*, another preparation in which the effect of LSD (250 μg) on geniculate nucleus was similar to that in *a* and *b*. Time calibration *e* applies to *a* through *d*; calibration *h* applies to *f* and *g*. *m*, stimulus artefact; t_1, response of fast-conducting optic-nerve fibers; *r*, response of geniculate cell bodies and radiation fibers; S_1, synaptic potential; t_1, (a), response of fast-conducting optic-nerve fibers; t_2, (a), response of slow-conducting fibers antidromically stimulated. Labelling of waveform in *f* indicates components of cortical evoked response. In these experiments effects of LSD are demonstrable only on the postsynaptic response of the lateral geniculate body. From Bishop *et al.,* 1959.

retinal level of the visual pathway, and this action combined with the blocking effect of LSD on geniculate synapses provides a basis for interpreting the dramatic visual unresponsiveness and blindness observed in animals following extraordinarily high doses (1 mg/kg) of LSD (Evarts, 1958).

Studies from the author's laboratory that were reported more than a decade ago emphasized the necessity of examining the effects of low concentrations of LSD on the visual and auditory systems of

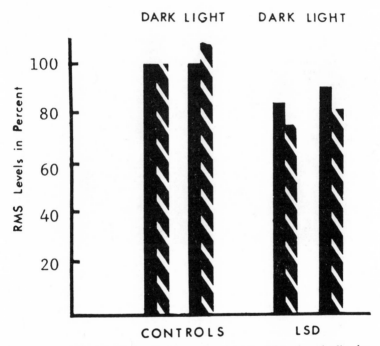

Fig. 4. Combined tonic discharge levels of eight chronically implanted, unanaesthetized cats under various experimental conditions. Solid bar, optic-tract integrated activity; striped bar, lateral geniculate body activity. Responses were recorded with bipolar electrodes in optic tract and lateral geniculate body. Amplified signals were led through a band-pass filter (500-10,000 cycle/sec band width) into an RMS meter. The voltage output of the meter is directly proportional to the average impulse rate. The RMS output was fed into a driver amplifier, which in turn operated an electromechanical integrator set for an integration time of 10 sec. Dark and light refer to environmental conditions. Modified from Schwartz and Cheney, 1965*b*.

unanaesthetized animals (Purpura, 1956). In these investigations as little as 2-5 µg/kg of LSD produced enhancement of the primary visual and auditory evoked responses (*Figure 5*). Increases in excitability in these pathways were demonstrable by examination of changes in testing responses produced by conditioning stimulation. Comparisons of the changes in auditory and visual evoked responses under LSD revealed dose-dependent differential effects. With concentrations of 30 µg/kg of LSD depression of primary

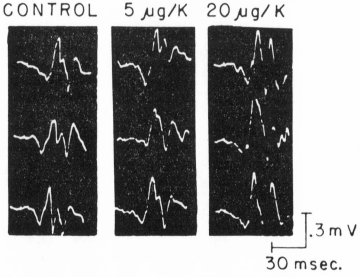

CONTROL   5 µg/K   20 µg/K

.3 m V

30 msec.

Fig. 5. The effect of LSD on evoked responses of visual cortex to photic stimulation in an unanaesthetized cat. Negativity upwards in these monopolar recordings. Control responses show typical early positive-negative components followed by a "W"-shaped late response. LSD injections result in increase in amplitude of early and late components of the evoked response. From Purpura, 1956.

auditory evoked responses was observed at a stage when visual responses exhibited continued enhancement. In these investigations doses as high as 60 µg/kg failed to produce significant depression of visual responses. These observations have been confirmed in part in studies carried out on unanaesthetized rabbits with chronically implanted electrodes located on the visual cortex (*Figure 6*: Koella and Wells, 1959). The latter investigations also confirmed the finding that the presence of anaesthesia increases the tendency of LSD to exert depressant effects on visual evoked responses.

Since the discovery of the markedly different effects produced by LSD in anaesthetized and unanaesthetized animals attention has been directed to changes in the variability of evoked responses observed after LSD in different environmental conditions. This is illustrated by experiments in which effects of LSD were tested on evoked responses recorded in the cochlear nucleus in unanaesthe-

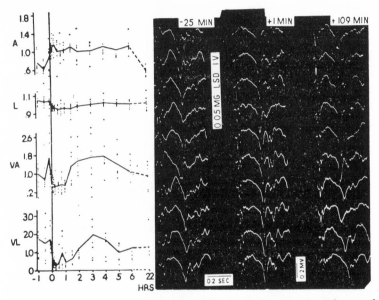

Fig. 6. Left: time course of the amplitude *A*, latency *L*, variance of amplitude *VA* and variance of latency *VL* of primary response of optically evoked cortical potentials before and after injection of 35 μg LSD. Normalized values on the ordinate; recording periods (1-16) and time on the abscissa. *Dots* show means of ten signals in each of the seven animals studied; *full line* connects mean values for all seven animals. Right: cortical, optically evoked potentials before (−25 min) and 1 min and 109 min after injection of LSD (50 μg) into unanaesthetized rabbit. Ten consecutive sweeps at 5-sec intervals. Stimulus coincides with left end of sweep. Note irregularity in amplitude of primary, secondary and late responses before injection (*left side column*). Late response also reveals irregular latency. Note "stabilizing" effect of LSD on these indicators (*middle column*). Partial recovery in 109-min record. From Koella and Wells, 1959.

tized animals under sound-proofed conditions and in the open laboratory (Key, 1965). It could be shown in these studies that LSD (10 µg/kg, given intraperitoneally) produced a significant increase in the mean amplitude of potentials evoked in the dorsal cochlear nucleus by tonal pip stimulation. When the experiment was transferred to the open laboratory, the enhancement of the primary responses by LSD was replaced by an increased variability in the amplitude of responses. Such effects were observed at all stations of the auditory projection system and were abolished by barbiturate anaesthesia. These and other experiments on LSD in animals under different environmental conditions suggest that the variability in amplitude of evoked response in a primary pathway that is seen after small doses of LSD is not due to a direct effect of the drug on the primary pathway. Rather it has been proposed that LSD produces such effects by interfering with more complex neuronal organizations capable of regulating the flow of afferent and efferent activity in the brain (Key, 1965). Several organizations that appear to be particularly prepotent in this regard comprise the so-called thalamic and brain-stem "reticular systems." It is appropriate therefore to examine the manner in which LSD influences activity characteristically associated with these "systems."

STUDIES OF LSD'S EFFECTS ON THALAMIC AND BRAIN-STEM RETICULAR PROJECTION SYSTEMS

It has been known for many years that low-frequency stimulation of medial and intralaminar nonspecific nuclei of the thalamus produces widespread synchronization of the electrical activity of the brain (Purpura, 1959). In contrast, high-frequency stimulation of the same thalamic regions or medial brain-stem reticular areas produces a pattern of EEG-desynchronization and an associated behavioral change in animals seen in arousal (Jasper, 1949; Moruzzi and Magoun, 1949). A vast literature has accumulated on the role of nonspecific projection systems in the maintenance of a wide variety of behavioral activities. Limitations of space permit reference here only to the most obvious relationships of these thalamic and brain-stem systems to processes involved in transitions from wakefulness to sleep and to the role of "reticular systems" in the establishment of conditional responses, learning, *etc.* (Jasper,

Proctor, Knighton, Noshay and Costello, 1958; Magoun, 1963). In view of the important role that thalamic and brain-stem non-specific projection systems play in the integrative functions of the brain, it is perhaps not surprising that some of the most dramatic effects of LSD reported to date have been observed on activities involving these systems (Bradley and Elkes, 1957; Himwich, 1956; Purpura, 1956).

Low-frequency stimulation of medial thalamic nuclei elicits a characteristic type of activity in the cerebral cortex that has been termed the recruiting response. The mechanism underlying the production of this synchronizing activity in the cortex has now been examined with intracellular recording techniques at the thalamic (Purpura and Cohen, 1962) and the cortical levels (Purpura, Shofer and Musgrave, 1964). Suffice it to say that synchronization of thalamic neuronal activity is effected by activation of neuronal organizations, which induce unique temporal sequences of EPSP's and IPSP's in a large proportion of thalamic cells, some of which have projections to cortex. At the cortical level the synchronized discharge of thalamic neurons results in the production of synaptic activities that are confined for the most part to axodendritic synaptic sites on cortical neurons (Purpura and Shofer, 1964). The effects of LSD on thalamocortical recruiting responses in lightly anaesthetized animals are reflected in suppression of these evoked potentials (*Figure 7*: Purpura, 1956). Less prominent effects of LSD on recruiting responses have been reported in studies of un-anaesthetized animals (Evarts, 1958).

It cannot be inferred that the depressant effect of LSD on re-cruiting responses is attributable solely to an action on the thalamic synchronizing mechanism or on cortical neurons. It has been shown by several groups of investigators that LSD induces an elec-trographic picture of EEG-desynchronization that is typically asso-ciated with alertness or arousal (Bradley and Elkes, 1957; Him-wich, 1956). Inasmuch as activation of brain-stem reticular regions antagonizes effects of thalamocortical synchronization (Moruzzi and Magoun, 1949), it seems likely that the depression of recruit-ment observed after LSD in lightly anaesthetized animals is largely attributable to a similar process of brain-stem reticular activation.

The literature on the effects of LSD on evoked potentials con-tains nothing more impressive than the observation on the exquisite

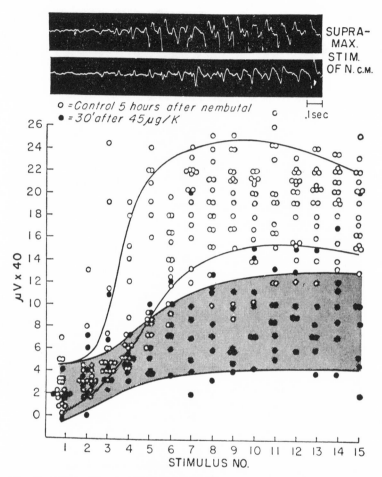

Fig. 7. The effects of LSD on recruiting responses in sensori-motor cortex evoked by low-frequency (10/sec) stimulation of medial non-specific thalamic nucleus, n. centrum medianum. Sample records show responses before LSD (*above*) and typical depression following LSD injection (*below*). Amplitudes of evoked recruiting responses in 10 to 12 series of stimulations before LSD are indicated with clear circle. Amplitudes of 7 to 9 series of stimulations after LSD shown in solid circles. Abscissa refers to the stimulus number in a single period of stimulation. Note that recruiting response attains maximal amplitude by the 5th to 7th stimulus of a 10/sec train. The mechanism of recruitment is not affected by LSD, but the maximal amplitude of recruiting responses is severely depressed in lightly anaesthetized preparations.

From Purpura, 1956.

sensitivity of reticulocortical evoked responses to LSD. The experiment illustrated in *Figure 8* bears on this point. The response in question, the "secondary discharge," was shown nearly three

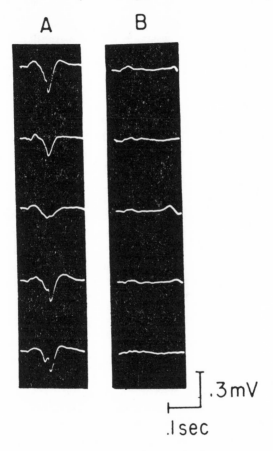

A. Control Sciatic S.D.
B. After LSD-25, 20μg/K I.V.

Fig. 8. The effects of LSD on generalized "secondary discharge" of neocortex to sciatic nerve stimulation in a cat anaesthetized with pentobarbital. *A*, response evoked every 5 sec by sciatic stimulation; *B*, administration of LSD abolishing this response, which involves medial brain-stem reticular organizations in its projection pathway to cortex.
From Purpura, 1956.

decades ago to be due to activity that does not utilize classical specific relay projections to cortex (Forbes and Morison, 1939). Identification of the "secondary discharge" as a reticulocortical response has been established (Purpura, 1955). The "secondary discharge" is best obtained under moderately deep barbiturate narcosis and is completely suppressed with transitions to the alert or aroused state. LSD in relatively low doses (10-20 µg/kg) completely blocks this response (Purpura, 1956), as would occur with reticulocortical activation. Recent studies (Roth, 1966) have confirmed the original observations of the author and have shown further that LSD in doses as low as 1-2 µg/kg produce a decrease in the average evoked "secondary discharge." Inasmuch as LSD can be shown to block nonspecific cortical responses involving brain-stem reticular projections, it is of further interest to note that the direct application of LSD to single unidentified neurons of the brain stem is capable of suppressing unit discharges evoked by nerve stimulation (Bradley and Wolstencroft, 1964). The relationship of this brain-stem unit suppression to the overt activation effects of LSD is not clear. Such findings, however, amply illustrate the difficulty of relating fundamentally different types of observations obtained under different experimental conditions.

PROBLEMS OF FURTHER ANALYSIS: LSD'S EFFECTS ON LIMBIC STRUCTURES

Thus far in this survey of the effects of LSD effects in experimental animals the results obtained in studies of specific or nonspecific evoked potentials have been described without reference to underlying physiological mechanisms. It may be noted that the LSD-induced depression of lateral geniculate postsynaptic responses to optic nerve stimulus has been interpreted as a competitive antagonism by LSD with the normal excitatory transmitter at these synapses (Bishop, Burke and Hayhow, 1959). Some support for this hypothesis has been forthcoming from observations on the partial recovery of LSD depression of geniculate postsynaptic responses by repetitive presynaptic nerve stimulation and asphyxiation. Both techniques antagonize the effects of curare at skeletal-muscle motor-end plates and may act similarly to antagonize a curare-like block produced by LSD on geniculate synapses (Bishop, Burke and

Hayhow, 1959; Evarts, 1958; Evarts, Landau, Freygang and Marshall, 1955).

To explain the more complex effects of LSD on other evoked activities would require consideration of the different synaptic organizations that contribute to different components of evoked potentials and more detailed analysis of the relationships of these potentials to the behavior of single neurons and neuronal networks. The fact that LSD changes an evoked potential or brain-wave pattern is sufficient evidence for an effect of this drug at the most pharmacologically sensitive site on the neuron, which is at the synapse. But it must be pointed out that enhancement of an evoked potential may occur by increasing excitatory synaptic activity or decreasing inhibitory activity in a particular neuronal population, or *vice versa*. As yet there is no evidence that LSD can excite neurons by a direct depolarizing action of the drug on the neuronal membrane. Although LSD has been shown to depress or block discharges of single brain-stem (Bradley and Wolstencroft, 1964) and hippocampal neurons (Stumpf, 1964), there is no evidence that this effect is referable to an activation of inhibitory synapses by the drug.

Enhancement of a sensory evoked activity in the brain can occur as a result of blockade of inhibitory elements in a particular organization; and "depression" of a potential can be due to blockade of excitatory synapses or activation of inhibitory synapses. Even the possible reticular-activation effect of LSD may not involve a direct excitatory action of LSD on brain-stem neurons. More than a decade ago it was suggested on the basis of examination of LSD's effects on specific and nonspecific evoked activities that LSD exerted a predominant blocking effect on axodendritic synapses (Purpura, 1956; Purpura, 1957). Support for this view was obtained in studies involving injection of LSD directly into a small cortical artery in patients undergoing various neurosurgical procedures (Purpura, Pool, Ransohoff, Frumin and Housepian, 1957). In these investigations, which were carried out in man, responses attributable largely to axodendritic synaptic activity in cortex were examined during close arterial injection of LSD (*Figure 9*). The results were consistent in showing significant depression of axodendritic synaptic activity.

Since the demonstration of LSD's effects on cortical-surface evoked responses neurophysiological information has been obtained at an extraordinary rate on virtually all types of central nervous system activities, particularly in respect to the analysis of spontaneous and evoked brain waves. Recognition of the complexity of the mechanisms underlying even the most "elementary"

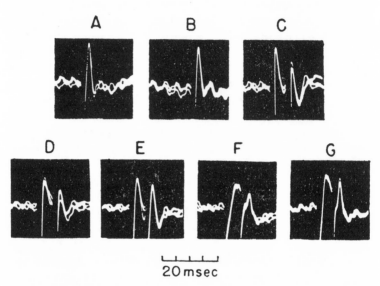

20 msec

Fig. 9. The effect of local cortical-arterial injection of LSD on axodendritic synapses involved in the superficial negative response of cortex. Negative responses were evoked by weak local cortical stimulation and were recorded from the surface of the frontal cortex in a patient undergoing psychosurgery (bimedial frontal lobotomy). *A*, conditioning; *B*, testing responses; *C*, together. Note augmentation of surface positive component of second response. *D*, reduction of both responses during rapid saline infusion and immediate recovery; *E* and *F*, 30 sec after 50 μg of LSD and *G*, 5 min later. The development of a detectable delay and abolition of the positive component (*F, G*) as well as a reduction of the negative components (*F*) is apparent. Three superimposed records throughout this series. From Purpura *et al.*, 1957.

neural events may render untenable many earlier notions concerning the mode of action of LSD and related agents. Clearly the neurophysiologist interested in further elucidating the mechanisms of LSD's action has two alternatives: either to probe more deeply into the basic electrophysiological changes in neurons and synapses produced by this agent, or to pursue experiments in which new analytical methods can be applied to the detection of subtle LSD-induced alterations in brain waves in particular structures known to exhibit unique types of electrical activity in association with controlled behavioral situations. At the present writing the author is unaware of studies of the former type, in which intracellular recording and stimulating techniques are being employed in order to clarify further LSD's actions on membrane properties and synaptic potentials. Perhaps the lack of such studies reflects a certain disenchantment with the notion that the complex behavioral disturbances produced by LSD can be meaningfully described in terms of alterations in the kinetics of ion movements at synapses and across cell membranes. Nonetheless, these effects are precisely what is to be expected of pharmacological agents with CNS actions, whether they be chemically simple agents, such as ethyl alcohol, or complex drugs like LSD (Grundfest, 1966).

In contrast to the present paucity of basic single-cell electrophysiological studies with LSD, the application of powerful computational techniques for brain-wave analysis in behavioral studies of LSD's effects in' animals has been seen during the past few years. It is of interest to survey several of these studies in order to obtain an overview of the capability of computational methods in detecting subtle alterations in brain function in association with LSD-induced changes in behavior. The analysis can be initiated by pointing out findings that indicate a close relationship between the presence of certain specified patterns of brain-wave activity in the hippocampal system and the ability of an animal to make a discriminative motor performance (Adey, Dunlop and Hendrix, 1960). In these studies electrical activity in the hippocampus and in related structures was recorded in animals with chronically implanted electrodes. The limbic structures were selected for examination because of the role played by these brain regions in various types of discriminative behavior. It has been reported that the distribution and characteristics of hippocampal "theta" waves, *i.e.,* slow-frequency (3–7 per second) waves, changes during learning the approach performance. In the phases between trials a spectrum of slow waves between 4 and 7 cycles per second is observed, and this is replaced with a regular burst of waves at 5.5 to 6.5 cycles per second during the approach performance. This burst of waves apparently persists unaltered in the hippocampal system in a high degree of overtraining (Adey and Walter, 1963).

Initial observations on the manner in which LSD (25 μg/kg) disrupts discriminative test situations in animals indicated the development of brief seizure-like episodes in hippocampal recordings in animals kept in a quiet environment (Adey, Bell and Dennis, 1962). The induction of seizures appeared to be dependent upon reduction of visual and auditory sensory influences. High doses of LSD (100 μg/kg) produced seizure patterns in hippocampal regions and in related structures, and such seizure episodes markedly interfered with the performance during the period in which a discrimination was required of the animal. Additional investigations have been directed toward detection of long-term actions of LSD (Adey, Porter, Walter and Brown, 1965). It is of interest in these studies that under "resting" conditions records taken immediately prior to testing an animal in a T-maze and compared for days before and after LSD with those taken one to two hours after injection of LSD revealed no differences. On the other hand, computed averages of hippocampal activity during a discriminative performance were modified in the days following LSD as shown in *Figures 10* and *11*. These computed averages showed increased amplitude in early waves for four and six days after LSD and sometimes longer than this. The point of emphasis here is that while it is not possible to detect persisting changes in brain-wave activity in *routine records* following LSD injections, computed averages of hippocampal theta waves *accompanying a discriminative performance* are clearly indicative of persisting changes that may underlie the well known behavioral tolerance to LSD following a single dose of the drug (Adey, Porter, Walter and Brown, 1965). It has also been pointed out in these investigations that different brain regions exhibit a differential susceptibility to LSD, with prominent effects being observed in the hippocampus. The findings that LSD may produce prolonged but subtle changes in the electrical activity recorded from limbic structures and related organizations during specific behavioral situations have been incorporated into a more general hypothesis based on additional studies of changes in tissue impedance (Adey, Kado, McIlwain and Walter, 1966). It has been proposed that LSD may produce long-term alterations in EEG patterns by changing the impedance

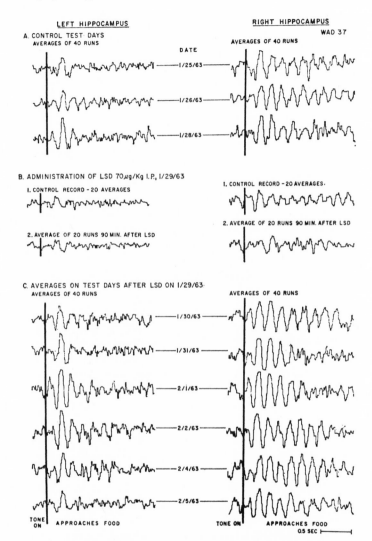

Fig. 10. Computed averages of epochs of left and right hippocampal EEG records during approach performance on days before LSD (*A*), the day of LSD dosage (*B*), and days after LSD (*C*). There was an increase in the amplitude and the regularity of the averages following LSD. This maximized three days after the drug (*C*, 2/1/63) and declined thereafter. From Adey *et al.*, 1965.

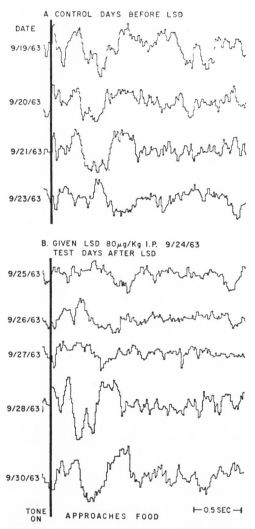

Fig. 11. Averages of forty daily trials in a dorsal hippocampal lead exhibiting essentially irregular activity in the EEG records. As in more regular EEG records, the average showed increased amplitude in early waves four and six days after LSD (9/28/63 and 9/30/63). From Adey *et al.,* 1965.

characteristics (conductivity) of extracellular and interglial compartments. Thus in addition to direct effects at synaptic sites, LSD may, in some fashion, alter the physicochemical properties of the poorly characterized material in the 200-ångstra spaces between presynaptic and postsynaptic elements and other membrane appositions (Adey, Kado, McIlwain and Walter, 1966). If such is the case, the problem of defining the long-term actions of LSD may depend upon obtaining more detailed information on the physicochemical nature of intercellular and subsynaptic gap material and the alterations in the electrical properties of this material produced by LSD and related agents.

COMMENTS AND CONCLUSIONS

Different operational methods have disclosed a wide variety of LSD's effects in neurophysiological studies in animals, and some of these effects have been reproduced in man under special experimental conditions. Despite the wealth of data on this subject a coherent and generally acceptable picture of the manner in which LSD exerts its effect on higher nervous functions remains obscure. That the prominent visual disturbances induced by LSD reflect varying degrees of alterations in the functional activity of elements at all stations in the visual pathway from retina to cortex is now established. But which behavioral signs of LSD are attributable to which actions at what synaptic station cannot be evaluated from present data. Excitatory and inhibitory synaptic interactions occur at all subcortical and cortical stations in a projection pathway. Thus LSD-induced blockade or activation of one or another synaptic site can lead to profound disorganizations of the temporal and spatial patterns of impulse activity in the projection pathway. The experimental methods that have been employed in testing for LSD's effects on neuronal organizations to date have generally been primitive in comparison to the refined analytical techniques currently used in studying neurophysiological mechanisms of information-coding in neural systems activated by physiological modes of stimulation. It seems likely that the application of these powerful new computational methods to studies of LSD's effects on patterns of unit discharge will provide important information that has not been forthcoming from previous studies of gross potentials evoked by volley stimulation of central or peripheral pathways.

Perceptual disturbances produced by LSD obviously involve more than the neural machinery comprising the classical visual pathway. Insofar as activation of a considerable proportion of the neuraxis from mesencephalon to forebrain occurs as a consequence of a particular visual stimulus, it is well to keep in mind the involvement of diffusely organized nonspecific projection systems in the overt manifestations of the drug. The same undoubtedly holds true for LSD-induced disturbances in auditory, olfactory, gustatory and somatic sensations.

It is now an established principle of neurophysiology that complex control systems are continuously in operation in shaping, blocking or facilitating one or another channel of sensory information, and that this regulation of sensory input to the brain is variable under different conditions of sleep and wakefulness. Such mechanisms for controlling afferent input not only permit focussing of attention to a particular task or motor event, but also protect the brain from the cacaphonous interplay of the varied meaningless signals that continually bombard sensory receptors. Recent neurophysiological investigations indicate that much of the control of sensory input to the brain is regulated by projection pathways from nonspecific "reticular systems" to primary sensory neurons in the spinal cord and brain stem. Little imagination is required to envision the consequences of disturbances initiated by LSD in these "reticular systems," hence the emphasis placed here on those experimental studies that have suggested a major action of the drug on brain-stem reticular regions. For it is within these complex brain-stem networks that much of the synaptic business of integrating incoming and outgoing information is transacted, and it is here that LSD is most likely to cause profound physiological disturbances through its synaptic actions.

The limbic structures that rim the medial surface of the cerebral hemisphere have long been known to be involved in the most detailed expressions of emotional behavior. These structures with their connections from neocortex, hypothalamus and midbrain reticular regions comprise synaptic fields in which the capacity for emotional expression is generated. The fact that LSD can produce both short-term and long-term effects on the functional activity of a major component of the limbic system, *i.e.,* the hippocampus, serves to emphasize the participation of these structures together with the midbrain reticular organizations in the functional disturbances induced by LSD.

Finally, it seems hardly necessary to point out that only man possesses a "second signal system" for communicating the details of his innermost experiences and the alterations in sensorium produced by LSD. Clearly were it not for the fact that LSD is capable of powerfully affecting man's psyche, there probably would have been little interest in studying this drug from the neurophysiological standpoint in experimental animals. For while LSD in extremely small concentrations can produce a variety of neurophysiological disturbances in animals, it is certainly not unique in this respect. Actually, LSD shares these properties with other drugs, some of which lack the important psychotomimetic and hallucinogenic features of LSD that are demonstrable in man. What, then, has basic neurophysiology contributed to the understanding of LSD's effects on the higher nervous activities of man? Is it legitimate to extrapolate the diverse electrophysiological findings in different animal species to man? In principle the answer to this must be negative. But insofar as there are common substrates of behavior involving fundamentally similar neuronal organizations in all higher vertebrates, it would be surprising indeed if the *major* neurophysiological effects of LSD demonstrable in animals were not applicable to man.

REFERENCES

Adey, W. R., Bell, F. R., and Dennis, B. J. Effects of LSD-25, psilocybin and psilocin on temporal lobe EEG patterns and learned behavior in the cat. *Neurology,* 1962, *12*:591.

Adey, W. R., Dunlop, E. W., and Hendrix, C. E. Hippocampal slow waves; distribution and phase relations in the course of approach learning. *Arch. Neurol.,* 1960, *3*:74.

Adey, W. R., Kado, R. T., McIlwain, J. T., and Walter, D. O. The role of neuronal elements in regional cerebral impedance changes in alerting, orienting and discriminative responses. *Exp. Neurol.,* 1966, *15*:490.

Adey, W. R., Porter, R., Walter, D. O., and Brown, T. S. Prolonged effects of LSD on EEG records during discriminative performance in cat: evaluation by computer analysis. *Electroenceph. clin. Neurophysiol.,* 1965, *18*:25.

Adey, W. R., and Walter, D. O. Application of phase detection and averaging techniques in computer analysis of EEG records in the cat. *Exp. Neurol.* 1963, *7*:189.

Apter, J. T., and Pfeiffer, C. C. Some effects of hallucinogenic drugs on electrical activity of the visual pathways of cats. *Am. J. Ophthalmol.*, 1960, *43*:206.

Bishop, P. A., Burke, W., and Hayhow, W. R. Lysergic acid diethylamide block of lateral geniculate synapses and relief by repetitive stimulation. *Exp. Neurol.*, 1959, *1*:556.

Bradley, P. B., and Elkes, J. The effects of some drugs on the electrical activity of the brain. *Brain,* 1957, *80*:77.

Bradley, P. B., and Wolstencroft, J. H. The action of drugs on single neurons in the brain stem. In Bradley, P. B., Flügel, F., and Hoch, P. (eds.), *Neuropharmacology.* Amsterdam: Elsevier, 1964.

Eccles, J. C. *The Physiology of Nerve Cells.* Baltimore: Johns Hopkins, 1957.

Eccles, J. C. *The Physiology of Synapses.* Berlin: Springer-Verlag, 1964.

Evarts, E. V. Neurophysiological correlates of pharmacologically induced behavioral disturbances. *Res. Publ. Ass. nerv. ment. Dis.,* 1958, *36*:347.

Evarts, E. V., Landau, W., Freygang, W., Jr., and Marshall, W. H. Some effects of lysergic acid diethylamide and bufotenine on electrical activity in the cat's visual system. *Am. J. Physiol.,* 1955, *182*:594.

Forbes, A., and Morison, B. R. Cortical response to sensory stimulation under deep barbiturate narcosis. *J. Neurophysiol.,* 1939, *2*:112.

Grundfest, H. Comparative electrobiology of excitable membranes. In *Advances in Comparative Physiology and Biochemistry.* New York: Academic Press, 1966.

Himwich, H. E. In Cholden, L. (ed.), *Proceedings of the Round Table on LSD and Mescaline in Experimental Psychiatry.* London: Grune and Stratton, 1956.

Jasper, H. H. Diffuse projection systems: integrative action of the thalamic reticular system. *Electroenceph. clin. Neurophysiol.,* 1949, *1*:405.

Jasper, H. H., Proctor, L. D., Knighton, R. S., Noshay, W. C., and Costello, R. T. (eds.). *Reticular Formation of the Brain.* Boston: Little, Brown, 1958.

Key, B. J. Effect of LSD-25 on potentials in specific sensory pathways. *Brit. med. Bull.,* 1965, *21*:30.

Koella, W. P., and Wells, C. H. Influence of LSD-25 on optically evoked potentials in the nonanesthetized rabbit. *Am. J. Physiol.* 1959, *196*:1181.

Magoun, H. W. *The Waking Brain.* Springfield: C. A. Thomas, 1963.

Moruzzi, G., and Magoun, H. W. Brain stems reticular formation and activation of the EEG. *Electroenceph. clin. Neurophysiol.,* 1949, *1*:455.

Purpura, D. P. Further analyses of evoked "secondary discharge": a study in reticulocortical relations. *J. Neurophysiol.,* 1955, *18*:246.

Purpura, D. P. Electrophysiological analysis of psychotogenic drug action: I. Effect of LSD on specific afferent systems in the cat. *Arch. Neurol. Psychiat.,* 1956, *75*:122.

Purpura, D. P. Electrophysiological analysis of psychotogenic drug action: II. General nature of LSD action on central synapses. *Arch. Neurol. Psychiat.,* 1956, *75*:132.

Purpura, D. P. Experimental analysis of the inhibiting action of LSD on cortical dendritic activity. *Ann. N.Y. Acad. Sci.,* 1957, *66*:515.

Purpura, D. P. Nature of electrocortical potentials and synaptic organizations in cerebral and cerebellar cortex. *Int. Rev. Neurobiol.,* 1959, *1*:47.

Purpura, D. P. Comparative physiology of dendrites. In *Neurobiology.* New York: Rockefeller University Press, 1967 (in press).

Purpura, D. P., and Cohen, B. Intracellular recording from thalamic neurons during recruiting responses. *J. Neurophysiol.,* 1962, *25*: 621.

Pupura, D. P., Pool, J. L., Ransohoff, J., Frumin, M. J., and Housepian, E. M. Observations on evoked dendritic potentials of human cortex. *Electroenceph. clin. Neurophysiol.,* 1957, *9*:453.

Purpura, D. P., and Shofer, R. J. Cortical intracellular potentials during augmenting and recruiting responses: I. Effects of injected hyperpolarizing currents on evoked membrane potential changes. *J. Neurophysiol.,* 1964, *27*:117.

Purpura, D. P., Shofer, R. J., and Musgrave, F. S. Cortical intracellular potentials during augmenting and recruiting responses: II. Patterns of synaptic activities in pyramidal and nonpyramidal tract neurons. *J. Neurophysiol.,* 1964, *27*:133.

Ramón y Cajal, S. *Histologie du systéme nerveux de l'homme et des vertébres.* Paris: Maloine, 1909.

Roth, W. T. The effect of LSD, mescaline and d-amphetamine on the evoked "secondary discharge." *Psychopharmacologia* (Berl.), 1966, *9*:253.

Schwartz, A. S., and Cheney, C. Effect of LSD on the tonic activity of the visual pathways of the cat. *Life Sci.,* 1965a, *4*:771.

Schwartz, A. S., and Cheney, C. Retinal effects of high doses of LSD in the cat. *Exp. Neurol.,* 1965b, *13*:273.

Stumpf, Ch. Drug action on septal and hippocampal units. In Bradley, P. B., Flügel, F., and Hoch, P. (eds.), *Neuropharmacology.* Amsterdam: Elsevier, 1964.

11   The Behavioral Effects of Psychotogens

By MURRAY E. JARVIK

IN 1943 Albert Hofmann accidentally discovered the peculiar mental effects of lysergic acid diethylamide (LSD) and set off a train of events culminating in world-wide interest in the actions of this drug. For the first fifteen years LSD was primarily a laboratory curiosity with interest centering upon the bizarre effects produced by extremely minute doses, of the order of one-hundred-millionths of a gram. Then during the 1950's some psychiatrists felt that a drug that could produce such a marked change in perception and thinking as does LSD might be useful in the treatment of psychiatric disorders needing reorientation. The therapeutic applications of LSD have not been widely extended for a number of reasons, including the difficulties in obtaining the drug, legal restrictions and the psychotic reactions attendant upon its administration. Tolerance develops rather rapidly so that chronic administration becomes a problem. Nevertheless, the drug has been used in a variety of psychiatric conditions, including character disorders, alcoholism and depression and pain associated with terminal cancer in the work of Dr. Kurland and others.

An extension of these therapeutic applications is the self-administration of LSD (sometimes known as abuse) by individuals who are seeking a new experience. This has not been a problem until recent years. Physiological dependence, as with opiates and sedative hypnotics, does not occur, and the reasons for LSD's popularity are not easy to understand. Tremendous impetus was given to the use of LSD by individuals of artistic temperament with the publication of Aldous Huxley's *The Doors of Perception* in 1954. Another spur to popularity was provided by two psychologists, Timothy Leary and Richard Alpert, who had to leave their teaching posts at Harvard University after administering the drug to students. They reacted to this academic rejection by making LSD-taking the basis of an apparently increasingly popular cult with religious overtones. Although the Sandoz Company has discontinued production of LSD and possession of the drug is illegal in almost every state, its use has mushroomed among college populations and young people generally who are interested in unconventional new experiences and thrills. This, in turn, has aroused the interest of law-enforcement and legislative agencies and also of the press. Adverse publicity has made genuine scientific research on this extremely important compound difficult.

Two properties of this drug have been largely responsible for interest among investigators: (1) its extreme potency, which has stimulated pharmacologists and physiologists to look for mechanisms of action; and (2) the psychotic state that it produces, which has made psychiatrists and psychologists curious about the nature of the behavioral changes and their possible relationship to naturally occurring psychoses. Other purer scientists saw the drug as a tool to manipulate and analyze behavior. LSD's dramatic and bizarre psychological actions, still the basis of its importance, were revealed almost at the moment of its inception.

HISTORY

In 1943 Albert Hofmann, a chemist working at Sandoz Pharmaceuticals in Basel, Switzerland, accidentally discovered the peculiar mental effects of LSD. He was searching for a stimulant resembling nikethamide and felt that if the diethylamide component of nikethamide were transferred to lysergic acid, the basic moiety of the ergot preparations, an interesting analeptic would perhaps be evolved. While working with this synthetic compound, which he had first synthesized in 1938, Hofmann found his own psychic state changed, and he describes it as follows:

> In the afternoon of 16 April, 1943, when I was working on this problem, I was seized by a peculiar sensation of vertigo and restlessness. Objects as well as the shape of my associates in the laboratory, appeared to undergo optical changes. I was unable to concentrate on my work. In a dream-like state I left for home where an irresistible urge to lie down overcame me. I drew the curtains and immediately fell into a peculiar state similar to a drunkenness, characterized by an exaggerated

imagination. With my eyes closed, fantastic pictures of extraordinary plasticity and intensive color seemed to surge towards me. After two hours this state gradually wore off.

Sometime thereafter, Hofmann was brave enough to put the proposition that LSD might be responsible for his state to a scientific test. He took 250 µg of the substance, and his previous experience was repeated with giddiness, restlessness, difficulty in concentration, visual disturbances and laughter. This discovery set off a train of events culminating in world-wide interest in the actions of this drug, and the era of LSD had begun.

Hofmann and his Swiss pharmacological colleagues at Sandoz, Stoll and Rothlin, very quickly recognized that the syndrome that LSD produced resembled that known for more than a century to be produced by mescaline and cannabis. The main difference was the extreme potency of the new compound. To this date the potency of LSD has never been exceeded, although other new and interesting psychotogenic substances have been discovered.

There has been a plethora of anecdotal papers describing subjective changes following LSD and confirming Hofmann's original descriptions. It is much harder to find psychological investigations in which the incidence and degree of behavioral change have been measured. The psychological studies on man with LSD can be classified at three levels according to the degree of objective quantification. The most numerous and most primitive are the clinical psychiatric descriptive accounts. Second, somewhat more sophisticated, are the studies involving the use of scales or questionnaires. Third, there are objective measures of behavioral responses. We shall consider these classes of data in turn.

The descriptive reports (Stoll, 1947; Becker, 1949; Forrer and Goldner, 1951; Rinkel *et al.*, 1952; Gastaut *et al.*, 1953; Rinkel, 1956; Carlson, 1957; Freeman, 1958) indicate that ingestion of LSD is followed after some minutes by very unpleasant symptoms —nausea, sometimes vomiting, headache, chills, tingling, sweating and a variety of other sensations implicating the autonomic nervous system. Pupillary dilatation always occurs, and tremor and dry mouth are common. Some degree of insomnia the night after taking LSD is also almost inevitable.

Change in mood is the first characteristically evident change in behavior (Delay and Pichot, 1951; Rinkel *et al.*, 1952; Anderson and Rawnsley, 1954; Elkes *et al.*, 1954; Abramson *et al.*, 1955*c, e;* Slater *et al.*, 1957). A drugged subject, particularly in a socially facilitating situation, usually becomes extremely emotional with uncontrollable laughing or crying. He may be very happy or extremely unhappy. Depending upon susceptibility and dose, he may be more or less responsive to his environment. Thus a mildly humorous remark or even one that is not ordinarily humorous may set off gales of laughter or torrents of tears. Belligerency may sometimes arise, and communication may become impossible. Subjects may assume unusual postures, slouching on chairs or lying on the floor.

On the subjective side, perceptual changes, particularly distortions and hallucinations in the visual sphere, have been most often noted (Stoll, 1949; Delay and Pichot, 1951). Although the visual changes have been discussed most frequently by investigators, it is likely that tactile sensibility is more universally affected (Jarvik, 1958). Hallucinations, the report of perception of formed objects that nobody else can perceive, are the most dramatic symptoms. Formed hallucinations, incidentally, are relatively uncommon. Only three out of sixty subjects given LSD at Mt. Sinai Hospital had true hallucinations, but when they do occur, they are hard to ignore. This low incidence may have been a function of the business-like hospital-laboratory atmosphere. Auditory hallucinations seem to be even less frequent than visual ones, indicating an important difference between LSD-induced psychoses and the naturally occurring ones, such as schizophrenia, where patients are more prone to hear voices than to see little men on the wall.

The ingestion of LSD by and large impairs intellectual processes (Jarvik *et al.*, 1955*a, b, c;* Kornetsky *et al.*, 1957), resulting in confusion, inappropriateness of action and difficulty in thinking. The role of motivational factors is not easy to assess. The subject either cannot or will not perform a task. I once offered a group of twelve drugged subjects ten dollars each if they could surpass their last placebo performance on an arithmetic test. None of them succeeded, though later, when the drug had worn off, they said that they had been trying. On the other hand, the extraordinary state sometimes inspires the production of unusual works of art or poetry (Matefi, 1952; Berlin *et al.*, 1955; Roubicek, 1956). Facilitation of creativity is one argument that has been given for encouraging widespread use of the psychotogens.

In 1953 Dr. Harold Abramson, Dr. Margaret Ferguson and I felt that a quantitative measure of symptoms would be useful, and we devised a questionnaire that we administered to our subjects at the Mt. Sinai Hospital (Abramson *et al.*, 1955*d, e*). The questionnaire has been the most sensitive, the easiest to apply and the most useful psychological procedure that we have employed to detect drug effects. Variations of our scale have subsequently been

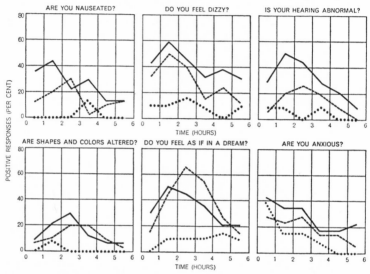

Fig. 1*: Sample questionnaire responses. Note how the peak incidence is a function of time after the drug was taken.

used by others, most notably by Isbell and his collaborators (1961) at Lexington, Kentucky, to compare other drugs with LSD. The questionnaire can be used to study time-dose relationships. Reports of nausea and dizziness appear to peak in the first hour or two (Fig. 1), whereas visual alterations and dreamlike states are reported to be maximal between two and three hours. Reports of anxiety are maximal at the beginning of the experiment even after administration of a placebo. There is a fairly close correspondence between objective effects like pupil size and questionnaire scores (Fig. 2).

* Figures 1, 2, 3 and 6 in this article reprinted by permission from Barron, F., Jarvik, M. E., and Bunnell, S., Jr. The hallucinogenic drugs. *Scientific American*, April, 1964. Copyright © 1964 by Scientific American, Inc. All rights reserved.

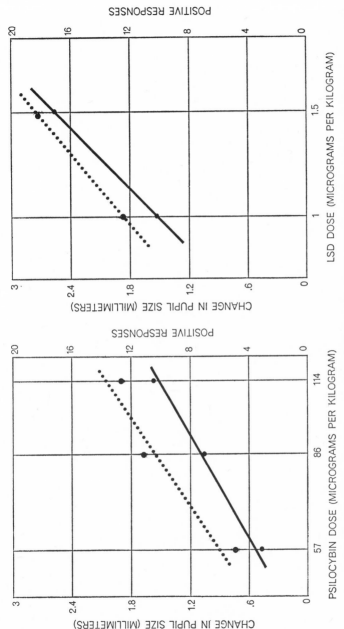

Fig. 2: Dose-related effects of LSD on pupillary size and questionnaire responses. This experiment was conducted by Harris Isbell of the University of Kentucky.

Figure 3, adapted from the work of Isbell, shows how the questionnaire may be used to reveal the psychological effects of different compounds. The lightest grey band represents a relative score on the questionnaire, with d-LSD and placebo as standards. It can be seen immediately that l-LSD and 2-brom-LSD are inactive, whereas the lysergic acid monoethylamide has a psychological effect slightly resembling that of LSD. The black bar represents the toxicity; the dark grey bar, the fever-producing ability; and the light grey, the antiserotonin potency.

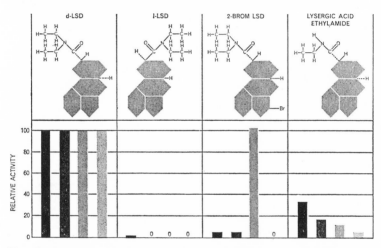

Fig. 3: Structure-activity relationships of congeners of LSD. Only a slight change in the molecule can markedly change the properties of the drug. Under each drug are shown four bar graphs depicting in order (1) toxicity, (2) hyperthermic effect, (3) anti-serotonin potency, and (4) psychotogenic activity.

We have also used the questionnaire to study the relative actions of other drugs (Fig. 4). We have given ten different drugs, including such well known substances as ethyl alcohol, methamphetamine, the monoethylamide and the 2-brom-LSD derivative, to a small group of subjects (and giving them a substitute for LSD) (Jarvik *et al.,* 1955). In Figure 5 the symptoms have been arbitrarily divided into three groups. The relative potency of these agents is apparent. Although LSD was given in the smallest dose and alcohol in the largest, the responses given under LSD are by far the greatest. It can be clearly distinguished from all the other drugs, even though they were administered in quite high doses.

A wide variety of agents has been studied during recent years because of their psychotogenic, psychotomimetic or hallucinogenic effects. One of these is piperidyl benzilate or JB329 (Ditran), a

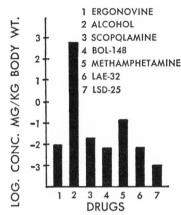

Fig. 4*: Logarithm of the concentration of seven drugs (mg/kg). Compare especially the relative potency of (2) alcohol and (7) LSD.

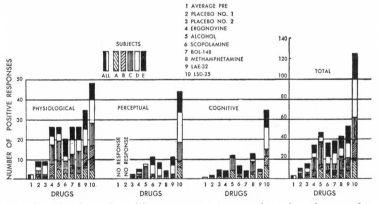

Fig. 5*: Number of positive responses to questionnaire given under ten different conditions.

* Reprinted by permission from Jarvik, M. E., Abrahamson, H. A., and Hirsch, M. W. Comparative subjective effects of seven drugs including lysergic acid diethylamide (LSD-25). *J. abnorm. soc. Psychol.*, 1955, *51*:657-662.

cholinergic blocking agent resembling the belladonna alkaloids scopolamine and atropine. It can be seen in Table I that the perceptual effects are significantly greater for LSD than for Ditran (Wilson and Shagass, 1964). Other studies have shown that it is hard to fool sophisticated subjects by giving them a substitute for LSD. Experienced subjects can tell when they have received as little as 20 µg of LSD by mouth. Just as the human nose is more

TABLE I
Mean Score Changes in Subsections
of Jarvik Questionnaire

Question Type	LSD	Ditran
Physical	4.4	5.1
Perceptual	9.3	6.3
Cognitive	1.6	0.3

From Wilson and Shagass, 1964.

sensitive to odors than a machine (and the bloodhound's nose even more so), the human brain appears to be especially sensitive to LSD.

A questionnaire is extremely useful for certain purposes, although it is no substitute for objective psychological measures in discovering how psychological functions are actually affected. Just because a subject feels that his vision is poor does not mean that it really is. In fact, it has been shown by a small number of investigators that psychological functions can be markedly influenced, sometimes impaired and sometimes improved, by LSD. On the basis of a large number of objective tests administered to subjects, we found that LSD interfered rather severely with some functions and not at all with others. For example, simple arithmetic ability was very susceptible to LSD in proportion to the dose (Jarvik *et al.,* 1955c), but digit span was not at all shortened (Jarvik *et al.,* 1955b). On the other hand, recall of nonsense syllables was significantly impaired, as were a number of complex visual discrimination tasks (Jarvik *et al.,* 1955b). Certain kinds of simple reaction time and the complex visual motor coördination involved in the pursuit-rotor task were not affected (Abramson *et al.,* 1955b, c). This differential effect of LSD is shown in Figure 6, in which the effects of LSD on a variety of memory tests are compared.

By and large, perception has been shown to be impaired by LSD. Dark adaptation is prolonged (Ostfeld, 1961), and the brightness threshold is increased. On the other hand, Landis and Clauses (1954) showed that LSD improves discrimination of flicker, *i.e.,* it raises the critical flicker-fusion threshold. Keeler (1963) has shown similar enhancement for psilocybin, another psychotogenic drug, and Aiba (1959) for d-amphetamine.

The influence of LSD on perception of the vertical has been studied by Wapner and his colleagues (Liebert *et al.,* 1957). They

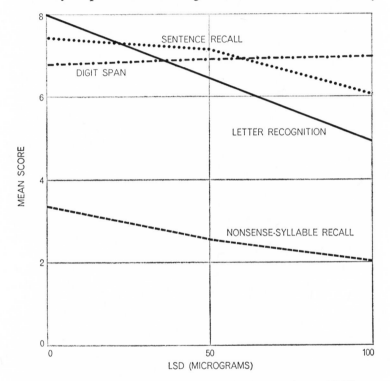

Fig. 6: Impairment of memory as a function of dose of LSD.

found that displacements of the vertical induced by bodily tilt were markedly increased by LSD. Also the effect of LSD upon perception of verticality was reported to be different in normals and schizophrenics.

LSD facilitated perception of the stabilized image. When an image is prevented from moving on the retina, it ordinarily fades out with the passage of time. LSD appears to maintain perception of this image. One reason advanced for this effect is that LSD increases the frequency of eye movements, which tend to facilitate perception during stabilized image experiments (Kohn and Bryden, 1965). Hebbard and Fisher (1966) also found that LSD, as well as psilocybin and mescaline, produces an increase in the frequency and the amplitude of saccadic movements of the eye.

Judgement of time became more variable with LSD (Boardman *et al.*, 1957; DeShon *et al.*, 1952). Time does not seem to move more slowly or more rapidly, but time estimates are more difficult.

LSD was found to have significantly greater effects on intellectual and perceptual tasks than secobarbital and chlorpromazine, whereas the latter two drugs affected motor tasks to a greater extent (Kornetsky *et al.*, 1957). Furthermore, LSD did not affect the continuous performance test, as did chlorpromazine (Primac *et al.*, 1957). Reaction time, tapping and handwriting have all been shown to be affected adversely by LSD (Hirsch *et al.*, 1956; Bercel *et al.*, 1956a, b). The effect of LSD on the Bender-Gestalt test was found to resemble that seen with schizophrenics (Abramson *et al.*, 1955e).

Relatively few studies have concerned themselves with the effects of drugs upon interpersonal communication. This is rather surprising, as most psychopharmaceuticals are given to individuals in situations in which they are interacting and will continue to interact with individuals. One such study is that of Lennard *et al.* (1956), who found that verbal communication, as analyzed by a modified Bales system of categories, was markedly modified by LSD. Because effected input and output of verbal material was modified by the drug, so was the total social behavior of the group. More studies in this area are clearly needed.

In summary, except for critical flicker-fusion frequency (CFF), all types of psychological tests, perceptual, motor and cognitive, have been shown to be impaired by LSD. Because LSD does have stimulant properties, it is entirely possible that optimal doses and optimal test parameters, which would produce facilitation, could be missed. This is rendered more likely in view of reports of facilitation of some types of performance in animals.

THE EFFECTS OF LSD ON ANIMALS

As might be expected, there is much more literature on controlled psychological experiments with animals than with humans.

The first generalization that one can make is that man seems to be much more sensitive to the effects of LSD than animals (Jarvik, 1958). This may have something to do with more efficient detoxification mechanisms in animals, but it may also be that the cerebral mechanisms attacked by LSD are better developed in man. As with man, the most commonly reported effects of LSD in animals are based on simple anecdotal reports of observation.

An intravenous injection of 1 mg/kg of LSD in the monkey caused visual disturbances, blindness and ataxia, plus a marked degree of tameness (Evarts, 1956). Another investigator reported slight withdrawal and catatonia in monkeys given LSD (Melander and Martens, 1958). In dogs LSD caused psychomotor excitement, followed by depression (Buscaino and Fronglia, 1953). Tolerance was noted on repeated administration. Ataxia, lack of reaction to pain and light and an increased reaction to sound was noted (Berenstein and Otero, 1958). Catatonia and irritation were seen in acute experiments, but in chronic experiments animals became tolerant (Jovanovic *et al.*, 1960). Intracerebral injections of 1-10 μg result in excitement, ataxia and various autonomic changes (Haley, 1956; Haley and McCormick, 1956; Bircher *et al.*, 1958). In cats LSD produced an increase in excitement, aggressive behavior and even rage (Bradley, 1957; Elder *et al.*, 1957; Gogerty *et al.*, 1957). It also reduced contentment and sociability (Norton and Tamburro, 1958), and it was reported to elicit spontaneous action potentials in the retina (Apter, 1957), with the conclusion that hallucinations originate in the retina. LSD injected into the ventricles produced initial restlessness, followed by drowsiness (Schwarz *et al.*, 1956; Haley, 1957). In rats LSD causes aggressiveness and hyperactivity (Brunad and Siou, 1959; Kment and Leibetseder, 1958).

LSD has been reputed to have aphrodisiac effects in man (Leary, 1966), but one investigator reported that sexual activity in rats was depressed by LSD (Gillette, 1960). On the other hand, Bignami (1966), working in Frank Beach's laboratory, reported that LSD, as well as a variety of other stimulants, increases the sexual activity of rats.

Woolley (1955) reported that mice given LSD intraperitoneally exhibited a peculiar backward gait. Mice with an inherited circling tendency (waltzing mice) stop circling after administration of LSD, but show an increased general excitatory state with erratic jerky movements (Rothlin and Cerletti, 1952). LSD inhibits circling movement in mice given imino-β-β-dipropionitrile (Widlocher *et al.*, 1957) and elicits circling movement in a certain strain of rats (Beluffi, 1956). In guinea pigs motor excitation was again seen with fairly large doses (Poloni and Maffezzoni, 1952). In rabbits excitation and sympathomimetic effects were seen after 100-200 mg/kg of LSD given intravenously (Shore and Brodie, 1957).

In pigeons 100-300 μg/kg of LSD increased the visual threshold without gross motor disturbance (Blough, 1957*a*). Larger doses produced catatonia in pigeons (Baruk *et al.*, 1958). In the salamander LSD impairs equilibrium (Peters and Vonderahe, 1956). The Siamese fighting fish *Betta splendens* in water with 0.2 μg/ml of LSD shows initial excitement and then rests vertically near the surface of the water (Abramson and Evans, 1954; Smith and Moody, 1956; Turner, 1956*a, b;* Trout, 1957). The guppy swims against obstacles and turns black (Keller and Umbreit, 1956). The discriminatory ability of ants is impaired by LSD (Staeger, 1958). Spiders can be given LSD in injected flies. They spin webs with characteristic patterns (Witt, 1956). Snails are very sensitive to LSD, and as little as 0.01 μg/cc causes a typical persistent disorganized movement of the gastropod (Abramson and Jarvik, 1955).

THE EFFECTS ON ELECTRICAL ACTIVITY OF THE BRAIN

LSD has some anticonvulsant effect in rabbits treated with topical applications of strychnine to the cortex. Adey *et al.* (1962) showed that in cats paroxysmal bursts of high-amplitude slow waves occurred, particularly with reduced light and sound. In the delayed response these bursts impaired behavior if they occurred during the retrieval interval, but not if they appeared during the retention interval. Many EEG studies show that LSD causes alerting and arousal. A male elephant was given 100 μg/kg (a total of 297 mg) of LSD in order to reproduce the signs of madness, but, unfortunately, it died (West *et al.*, 1962).

CONDITIONING AND LEARNING

Pole-climbing by trained rats is impaired by LSD. Hamilton (1960) found, however, that LSD facilitated escape reactions from electric shock. Cook and Weidley (1957) found that high doses of LSD blocked conditioned avoidance and escape responses in rats. On the other hand, Taeschler (1960) found that LSD significantly shortened jumping time to a rod. Key and Bradley (1958) found that 5 μg/kg of LSD in cats reduced the threshold for an unconditioned arousal response, but not for a conditioned arousal response. After 10-15 μg/kg, the cat remained alert for longer periods and was more responsive to stimuli. Jarvik and Chorover (1958) found that LSD impaired performance of a delayed alternation test in monkeys in doses as low as 5 μg/kg. Tolerance developed with injections on consecutive days. Fuster (1957; 1959) showed tachistoscopic perception was impaired by LSD in monkeys. LSD elevates the visual threshold in pigeons, but improves visual discrimination performance even though the rate of response is decreased (Blough, 1957a, b).

LSD impairs or depresses self-stimulation in rats and monkeys (Olds and Eiduson, 1957; Stein, 1960; Malis, 1960). Maffii (1959) found that 0.1 mg/kg of LSD shortened the learning time of a secondary conditioned escape response in rats.

Rapid tolerance has been demonstrated in man (Isbell *et al.,* 1955), in monkeys (Jarvik and Chorover, 1958, 1960), in dogs (Jovanovic *et al.,* 1960; Buscaino and Fronglia, 1953), in rats (Winter and Flataker, 1957; Freedman *et al.,* 1958) and in rabbits (Gogerty and Dille, 1956). A fluctuating tolerance has been demonstrated by some investigators (Koella and Bergen, 1966).

In summary then, LSD appears to produce excitant effects in animals, frequently manifested by an increase in aggression. Learning and performance are usually impaired, but under especial conditions may be facilitated. The practical consequences of experimental studies with this drug are that in animals the mechanism of action can be analyzed, because the drug may be given by a variety of routes. High, dangerous doses may be used, and physiological explorations may be made with impunity. In humans, experimental studies are of value, because they tell us what the drug really does. The importance of the placebo effect, of suggestion and social facilitation, is known to be tremendous. Well controlled experimental studies enable the scientist to disentangle these variables and to study the truly pharmacological actions of the drug. Whatever the practical value of LSD, it is a tremendously useful tool in the study of psychological processes. Even though the legal restrictions on its indiscriminate use by the public must be tightened, at the same time the rules should be modified so that basic research will not be inhibited. Only in this way can we learn how this fascinating drug really works.

REFERENCES

Abramson, H. A., and Evans, L. T. Lysergic acid diethylamide (LSD-25): II. Psychobiological effects on the Siamese fighting fish. *Science*, 1954, *120*:990.

Abramson, H. A., and Jarvik, M. E. Lysergic acid diethylamide (LSD-25): IX. Effect on snails. *J. Psychol.*, 1955a, *40*:337.

Abramson, H. A., Jarvik, M. E., and Hirsch, M. W. Lysergic acid diethylamide (LSD-25): X. Effect on reaction time to auditory performance. *J. Psychol.*, 1955b, *39*:455.

Abramson, H. A., Jarvik, M. E., and Hirsch, M. W. Lysergic acid diethylamide (LSD-25): X. Effect on reaction time to auditory and visual stimuli. *J. Psychol.*, 1955c, *40*:39.

Abramson, H. A., Jarvik, M. E., Kaufman, M. R., Kornetsky, C., Levine, A., and Wagner, M. Lysergic acid diethylamide (LSD-25): I. Physiological and perceptual responses. *J. Psychol.*, 1955d, *39*:3.

Abramson, H. A., Kornetsky, C., Jarvik, M. E., Kaufman, M. R., and Ferguson, M. W. Lysergic acid diethylamide (LSD-25): XI. Content analysis of clinical reactions. *J. Psychol.*, 1955e, *40*:53.

Abramson, H. A., Waxenberg, S. E., Levine, A., Kaufman, M. R., and Kornetsky, C. Lysergic acid diethylamide (LSD-25): XIII. Effect on Bender-Gestalt test performance. *J. Psychol.*, 1955f, *40*:341.

Adey, W. R., Bell, F. R., and Dennis, B. J. Effects of LSD-25, psilocybin and psilocin on temporal lobe EEG patterns and learned behavior in the cat. *Neurology*, 1962, *12*:591.

Aiba, S. The effects of dexamphetamine, sodium amobarbital, and meprobamate on critical frequency of flicker under two different surround illuminations. *Psychopharmacologia*, 1959, *1*:89.

Anderson, E. W., and Rawnsley, K. Clinical studies of lysergic acid diethylamide. *Mschr. Psychiat.*, 1954, *128*:38.

Apter, J. T. The effect of the hallucinogenic drugs LSD-25 and mescaline on the electroretinogram. *Ann. N. Y. Acad. Sci.*, 1957, *66*:508.

Baruk, H., Launay, J., Berges, J., Perles, R., and Conte, C. Étude preliminaire de l'action du L.S.D. 25 chez les animaux, catatonie experimentale chez le pigeon. *Ann. med. psychol.*, 1958, *116*:127.

Becker, A. M. Zur psychopathologie der lysergsaurediathylamidwirkung. *Wien Zschr. Nervenh.*, 1949 2:402.

Beluffi, M. Caratteristica azione della LSD Sandoz su di un particolare ceppo di ratti albini con risultante attivazione di peculiari anomale latenze motorie. *Nevrasse*, 1956, *6*: 225.

Bercel, N. A., Travis, L. E., Olinger, L. B., and Dreikurs, E. Model psychoses induced by LSD-25 in normals: I. Psychophysiological investigations, with special reference to the mechanism of the paranoid reaction. *Arch. Neurol. Psychiat.*, 1956, *75*:588.

Ibid. II. Rorschach test findings, 1956, *75*:612.

Berenstein, I., and Otero, T. Algunos efectos de la LSD 25 en el perro. *Acta neuropsiquiatr. argent.*, 1958, *4*:143.

Berlin, L., Guthrie, T., Weider, A., Goodell, H., and Wolff, H. G. Studies in human cerebral function: the effects of mescaline and lysergic acid on cerebral processes pertinent to creative activity. *J. Nerv. Ment. Dis.*, 1955, *122*:487.

Bignami, G. Pharmacologic influences on mating behavior in the male rat. *Psychopharmacologia*, 1966, *18*:44.

Bircher, R. P., Bartelstone, H. J., and Wang, S. C. Effects of lateral, third and fourth ventricle injections of cardiac glycosides and LSD in unanesthetized dogs. *Fed. Proc.*, 1958, *17*: 350.

Blough, D. S. Effects of drugs on visually controlled behavior in pigeons. In S. Garattini and V. Ghetti (eds.), *Psychotropic Drugs*. N.Y.: Elsevier, 1957*a*.

Blough, D. S. Effect of lysergic acid diethylamide on absolute visual threshold of the pigeon. *Science*, 1957*b*, *126*:304.

Boardman, W. K., Goldstone, S., and Lhamon, W. T. Effects of lysergic acid diethylamide (LSD) on the time sense of normals: A preliminary report. *Arch. Neurol. Psychiat.*, 1957, *78*:321.

Bradley, P. B. Recent observations on the action of some drugs in relation to the reticular formation of the brain. *EEG Clin. Neurophysiol.*, 1957, *9*:372.

Brunaud, M., and Siou, G. Action de substances psychotropes, chez le rat, sur un etat d'agressivite provoquee. In P. B. Bradley, P. Deniker and C. Radouco-Thomas (eds.), *Neuro-Psychopharmacology*. Amsterdam: Elsevier, 1959.

Buscaino, G. A., and Fronglia, N. Modificazioni biochimiche, electroencefalografiche, istrochimiche ed istopatologiche, in cani, durante l'intossicazione sperimentale acuta e cronica da dietilamide dell'acido lisergico. *Acta neurol. 8*:641.

Carlson, V. R. Individual pupillary reactions to certain centrally acting drugs in man. *J. Pharmacol. Exp. Thera.*, 1957, *121*:501.

Cook, L., and Weidley, E. Behavioral effects of some psychopharmacological agents. *Ann. N. Y. Acad. Sci.*, 1957, *66*:740.

Delay, J., and Pichot, P. Diethylamide de l'acide d-lysergique et troubles psychiques de l'ergotisme. *C.r. Soc. Biol.* 1951, *145*: 1609.

DeShon, H. J., Rinkel, M., and Solomon, H. C. Mental changes experimentally produced by L.S.D. (d-Lysergic acid diethylamide tartrate). *Psychiat. Quart.*, 1952, *26*:33.

Elder, J. T., Gogerty, J. H., and Dille, J. M. Survey of d-lysergic acid diethylamide (LSD) antagonists. *Fed. Proc.*, 1957, *16*:293.

Elkes, J., Elkes, C., and Bradley, P. B. The effect of some drugs on the electrical activity of the brain, and on behaviour. *J. Ment. Sci.*, 1954, *100*:125.

Evarts, E. V. Some effects of bufotenine and lysergic acid diethylamide on the monkey. *Arch. Neurol. Psychiat.*, 1956, *75*:49.

Forrer, G. R., and Goldner, R. D. Experimental physiological studies with lysergic acid diethylamide (LSD-25). *Arch. Neurol. Psychiat.*, 1951, *65*:581.

Freedman, D. X., Aghajanian, G. K., and Ornitz, E. M. Patterns of tolerance to lysergic acid diethylamide and mescaline in rats. *Science*, 1958, *127*:1173.

Freeman, H. Pupil dilatation in normal and schizophrenic subjects following lysergic acid diethylamide ingestion. *Arch. Neurol. Psychiat.*, 1958, *79*: 341.

Fuster, J. M. Tachistoscopic perception in monkeys. *Fed. Proc.*, 1957, *16*:43.

Fuster, J. M. Lysergic acid and its effect on visual discrimination in monkeys. *J. Nerv. Ment. Dis.*, 1959, *129*:252.

Gastaut, H., Ferrer, S., Castelis, C., Leserve, N., and Lushnat, K. Action de la diethylamide de l'acide d-lysergique (LSD-25) sur les fonctions psychiques et l'electroencephalogramme. *Confinia Neurol.*, 1953, *13*:102.

Gillett, E. Effects of chlorpromazine and d-lysergic acid diethylamide on sex behavior of male rats. *Proc. Soc. Exp. Biol. Med.*, 1960, *103*:392.

Gogerty, J. H., and Dille, J. M. Tolerance to the pyretogenic effects of lysergic acid diethylamide. *J. Pharmac. Exp. Therap.*, 1956, *116*: 450.

Gogerty, J. H., Elder, J. T., and Horita, A. Modifications of actions of LSD-25 by reserpine. *Fed. Proc.*, 1957, *16*:300.

Haley, T. J. Pharmacological effects from drugs injected intracerebrally in unanesthetized animals. *J. Am. pharm. Ass.*, 1956, *45*:604.

Haley, T. J. Pharmacological actions from intracerebral drug injections. In S. Garattini and V. Ghetti (eds.), *Psychotropic Drugs*. New York: Elsevier, 1957.

Haley, T. J., and McCormick, W. G. Intra-cerebral injection of LSD-25 in the unanesthetized dog. *Fed. Proc.*, 1956, *15*:433.

Hamilton, C. L. Effects of LSD-25 and amphetamine on a running response in the rat. *Arch. Gen. Psychiat.*, 1960, *2*:104.

Hebbard, F. W., and Fischer, R. Effect of psilocybin, LSD, and mescaline on small involuntary eye movements. *Psychopharmacologia*, 1966, *9*:146.

Hirsch, M. W., Jarvik, M. E., and Abramson, H. A. Lysergic acid diethylamide (LSD-25): XVIII. Effects of LSD-25 and six related drugs upon handwriting. *J. Psychol.*, 1956, *41*:11.

Huxley, Aldous. *The Doors of Perception.* New York: Harper, 1954.

Isbell, H., Fraser, H. F., Wikler, A., and Belleville, R. E. Tolerance to diethylamide of lysergic acid (LSD-25). *Fed. Proc.,* 1955, *14*: 354.

Isbell, H., Wolbach, A. B., Wikler, A., and Miner, E. J. Cross tolerance between LSD and psilocybin. *Psychopharmacologia,* 1961, *2*:147.

Jarvik, M. E. Are there any psychotherapeutic or psychotomimetic drugs? In H. Pennes (ed.), *Psychopharmacology: Pharmacological Effects on Behavior.* New York: Hoeber-Harper, 1958.

Jarvik, M. E., Abramson, H. A., and Hirsch, M. W. Lysergic acid diethylamide (LSD-25): IV. Effect on attention and concentration. *J. Psychol.,* 1955a, *39*:373.

Jarvik, M. E., Abramson, H. A., and Hirsch, M. W. Lysergic acid diethylamide (LSD-25): VI. Effect upon recall and recognition of various stimuli. *J. Psychol.,* 1955b, *39*:443.

Jarvik, M. E., Abramson, H. A., Hirsch, M. W., and Ewald, A. T. Lysergic acid diethylamide (LSD-25): VIII. Effect on arithmetic test performance. *J. Psychol.,* 1955c, *39*:465.

Jarvik, M. E., and Chorover, S. Effects of lysergic acid diethylamide upon certain aspects of memory (delayed alternation) in monkeys. *Fed. Proc.,* 1958, *17*:381.

Jarvik, M. E., and Chorover, S. Impairment by lysergic acid diethylamide of accuracy in performance of a delayed alternation test in monkeys. *Psychopharmacologia,* 1960, *1*:221.

Jovanovic, D., Kandic, B., and Kronja, T. Prilog ispitivanju dejstva LSD-25 u eksperimentu na psima. *Vojno-sanit. Pregl.* 1960, *17*: 419.

Keeler, M. H. Interrelations of the effects of psilocybin on subjective sensation, photopic critical frequency of fusion and circulating non-esterified fatty acides. *Experientia,* 1963, *19*:37.

Keller, D. L., and Umbreit, W. W. Chemically altered "permanent" behavior patterns in fish and their cure by reserpine. *Science,* 1956, *124*:407.

Key, B. J., and Bradley, P. B. Effect of drugs on conditioning and habituation to arousal stimuli in animals. *Nature,* 1958, *182*:1517.

Kment, A., and Leibetseder, J. Verhaltensphysiologische studien an ratten nach lysergsaure-diathylamid-(LSD)-verabreichung. *Abl. Veterinarmed.,* 1958, *5*:877.

Koella, W. P., and Bergen, J. R. Cyclic response to repeated LSD administration. In W. P. Koella and A. G. Karczmar (eds.), *Neurophysiological and Behavioral Aspects of Psychotropic Drugs* (papers presented at the A.C.N.P.P. Meeting: Workshops III— Neurophysiological Aspects of Drug Action—and V—Chemistry, Memory and Learning). December, 1966.

Kohn, B., and Bryden, M. P. The effect of lysergic acid diethylamide (LSD-25) on perception with stabilized images. *Psychopharmacologia,* 1965, *7*:311.

Kornetsky, C., Humphries, O., and Evarts, E. V. Comparison of psychological effects of certain centrally acting drugs in man. *Arch. Neurol. Psychiat.*, 1957, *77*:318.

Landis, C., and Clausen, J. Certain effects of mescaline and lysergic acid on psychological functions. *J. Psychol.*, 1954, *38*:211.

Leary, T. Interview. *Playboy*, September, 1966.

Lennard, H., Jarvik, M. E., and Abramson, H. A. Lysergic acid diethylamide (LSD-25): XII. A preliminary statement of its effects upon interpersonal communication. *J. Psychol.*, 1956, *41*: 185.

Liebert, R. S., Wapner, S., and Werner, H. Studies in the effects of lysergic acid diethylamide (LSD-25). Visual perception of verticality in schizophrenic and normal adults. *Arch. Neurol. Psychiat.*, 1957, *77*:193.

Maffii, G. Influenza della mescalina e della dietilamide dell'acido lisergico (LSD-25) sull'apprendimento del riflesso condizionato di salvaguardia primario e secondario) nel ratto. *Farmaco. Ed. sci.* 1959, *14*:503.

Malis, J. L., Brodie, D. A., and Moreno, O. M. Drug effects on the behavior of self-stimulation monkeys. *Fed. Proc.* 1960, *19*:23.

Matefi, L. Mescalin-und-lysergsaurediathylamid-Rausch: Selbetversuch mit besonderer berucksichtigung eines zeichentests. *Confinia neurol.*, 1952, *12*:146.

Melander, B., and Martens, S. The mode of action of taraxein and LSD. *Dis. Nerv. Syst.*, 1958, *19*:478.

Norton, S., and Tamburro, J. Effects of hallucinogens on spontaneous behavior patterns of animals. *J. Pharmac. exp. Ther.*, 1958, *122*: 57A.

Olds, J., and Eiduson, E. Selective effects of chemicals in the brain studied by techniques of self stimulation. *Excerpta Medica*, 1957.

Ostfeld, A. M. Effects of LSD-25 and JB318 on tests of visual and perceptual function in man. *Fed. Proc.*, 1961, *20*:876.

Peters, J. J., and Vonderahe, A. R. Behavior of the salamander under the influence of LSD-25 and Frenquel, and accompanying electrical activity of brain and spinal cord. *J. Nerv. Ment. Dis.*, 1956, *124*:69.

Poloni, A., and Maffezzoni, G. Le variazioni dell'attivita colinergica del tessuto cerebrale per effetto della bulbocapnina, della mescalina e della dietilamide dell'acido lisergico. *Sistema nerv.*, 1952, *4*:578.

Primac, D. W., Mirsky, A. F., and Rosvold, H. E. Effects of centrally acting drugs on two tests of brain damage. *Arch. Neurol. Psychiat.*, 1957, *77*:328.

Rinkel, M., DeShon, H. J., Hyde, R. W., and Solomon, H. C. Experimental schizophrenia-like symptoms. *Amer. J. Psychiat.*, 1952, *108*:572.

Rinkel, M. Biochemical reflections on the psychosis problem. In

Lysergic Acid Diethylamide and Mescaline in Experimental Psychiatry. New York: Grune & Stratton, 1956.

Rothlin, E., and Cerletti, A. Ueber einige pharmakologische untersuchungen an mausen mit congenitaler drehsucht. *Helv. Physiol. Acta*, 1952, *10*:319.

Roubicek, J. Experimental mental disorders. *Vesmir*, 1956, *35*:291.

Schwarz, B. E., Wakim, K. G., Bickford, R. G., and Lichtenheld, F. R. Behavioral and electroencephalographic effects of hallucinogenic drugs: Changes in cats on intraventricular injection. *Arch. Neurol. Psychiat.*, 1956, *75*:83.

Shore, P. A., and Brodie, B. B. LSD-like effects elicited by reserpine in rabbits pretreated with iproniazid. *Proc. Soc. Exper. Biol. Med.*, 1957, *94*:433.

Slater, P. E., Morimoto, K., and Hyde, R. W. The effect of group administration upon symptom formation under LSD. *J. Nerv. Ment. Dis.*, 1957, *125*:312.

Smith, K., and Moody, A. C. Schizophrenia and the Siamese fighting fish. *Dis. Nerv. Syst.*, 1956, *17*:327.

Staeger, R. Intoxicatiousversich mit ameisen. *Bull. Murithienne Fasc.*, 1958, *75*:8.

Stein, L. Self-selected brain stimulation reward threshold modified by drugs. *Fed. Proc.*, 1960, *19*:264.

Stoll, W. A. Lysergsaure-diathyl-amid, ein Phantastikum aus der Mutterkorngruppe. *Schweiz. Arch. Neru.*, 1947, *60*.

Stoll, W. A. Ein neues, in sehr kleinen Mengen wirksames Phantastikum. *Schweiz. Arch. Neur.*, 1949, *64*:483.

Taeschler, M., Weidmann, H., and Cerletti, A. Die wirkung von LSD auf die reaktionszeiten bei einer bedingten fluchtreaktion und im analgesietest. *Helv. physiol. parmacol. Acta*, 1960, *18*:43.

Trout, D. L. Interaction of serotonin and lysergic acid diethylamide in the Siamese fighting fish. *J. Pharmac. exp. Thera.*, 1957, *121*:130.

Turner, W. J. The effect of lysergic acid diethylamide on *Betta splendens*: I. *Dis. Nerv. Syst.*, 1956, *17*:193.

Turner, W. J. The effect of lysergic acid diethylamide on *Betta splendens*: II. Frenquel. *Dis. Nerv. Syst.*, 1956, *17*:198.

West, L. J., and Pierce, C. M. Lysergic acid diethylamide: its effects on a male Asiatic elephant. *Science*, 1962, *138*:1100.

Widlocher, D., Nakajima, H., and Thuillier, J. Action des monoethylamide (LAE) et diethylamide (LSD) de l'acide lysergique sur le comportement de la souris tournante provoquee par l'iminob-b-dipropionitrile. *Compt. rend. Soc. biol.*, 1957, *151*:668.

Wilson, R. E., and Shagass, C. Comparison of two drugs with psychotomimetic effects (LSD and Ditran). *J. Nerv. Ment. Dis.*, 1964, *138*:277 (Copyright © 1964 by The Williams and Wilkins Company).

Winter, C. A., and Flataker, L. Further experiments on the performance of trained rats treated with lysergic acid diethylamide. *J. Pharmac. exp. Thera.*, 1957, *119*:194.

Witt, P. N. *The Effect of Substances on the Construction of Webs by Spiders as a Biological Test.* Berlin: Springer, 1956.

Woolley, D. W. Production of abnormal (psychotic?) behavior in mice with lysergic acid diethylamide, and its partial prevention with cholinergic drugs and serotonin. *Proc. Nat. Acad. Sci.,* 1955, *41*:338.

12 Third Discussion

The moderator: Mr. Giarman mentioned persisting reactions from LSD, but he did not indicate whether he knew of any that had some chemical basis. Dr. Jarvik was rather skeptical about whether they occur, and if they occur, about whether one should treat them as drug effects or as a suggestibility phenomenon. May I ask each of you what you think about persisting reactions from LSD?

Mr. Giarman: To start off, it is a very important problem. I think that the current hypotheses were produced when pharmacological evidence first arose, as I mentioned. One of them was the so-called "trigger" hypothesis of LSD's action, which simply said that LSD triggers some phenomenon in the brain that far outlasts its chemical presence in the brain. Now, with some of the evidence I presented, which is, I think, a selection of the best data, one cannot support the trigger hypothesis with the chemical measurements that have been made; but I would hasten to say that they're measuring here very minute amounts of the substance, and there are limitations on the measuring techniques. So it's always possible that one could explain this on the basis of the continued presence of an unmeasurable amount of the stuff. I don't think, at the present time, however, that there is a good pharmacological explanation for this.

Dr. Purpura: I think we were all aware of long-persisting phenomena of the type you described from the very earliest introduction of the drug. From the neurophysiological standpoint, I don't believe that there is a single shred of evidence to indicate that there is a persisting effect directly referable to a behavioral situation in the animal. I think the data that some researchers have published, however, are very tenuous in respect to showing a persisting action, which they use to interpret the habituation or the tolerance mechanism, rather than any persisting behavioral effect. Obviously, when we look at any changes in brain waves or EEG, we are talking about chemistry and large molecules of one kind or another. So that if there is something, we haven't the operational methods to look at it in terms of straight neurophysiological actions. It may be that there are some very peculiar changes that go on in this intercellular-substance material, but this is going to take us into the kind of chemistry for which we need far more tools or better tools than there are at the present time. I couldn't say that there is a specific neurophysiological action that is a correlate of this repetitiveness of the response following a single drug injection.

The moderator: As I recall, from your data, the size of the area involved is about 2% of a single wave length of the light visible to us. Is that about the right description?

Dr. Purpura: 150 to 200 ångstra—that's the space. Most interactions that are going on between neurons are going to cross that space, which turns out to be a very important factor in interactions between neurons.

The moderator: So we don't have today physical tools to get at that, and we don't expect them next week or next decade.

Dr. Purpura: I think certainly in the next decade.

Mr. Giarman: I think you can expect these tools sooner than that. There are histochemical methods that are now being developed at a very rapid rate. As a matter of fact, there is a method that visualizes the substance that Dr. Purpura was talking about. Phosphotungstic acid, a reaction product, when used in electron-microscopy demonstrates that there is a protein substance there. It is, as Dr. Purpura pointed out, not an empty space. There is already electromicroscopic histochemical evidence that there is a substance there. What the interaction is is the question.

The moderator: Dr. Jarvik, from your experience, which would you choose, the pharmacological or the learning phenomenon as the most likely basis for these reports of persisting LSD effects?

Dr. Jarvik: I'm sure that they all can enter into it. The problem here is that we can't subject the phenomenon of long-term psychosis to an experimental test. We can't set up a control situation in which some individuals get LSD and some do not. We just have to look at the world as it is. There are some legal implications, because if the trigger hypothesis is true, there may be some basis for the restrictive legislation. If, in fact, a single dose of LSD can trigger a psychosis that would not otherwise occur, we should worry about it. Now, there is some analogy to this in other types of psychosis. Sometimes psychosis will develop after a woman has a baby, and it will persist. We don't know why. We don't know whether there's a long-term process or whether the individual was originally susceptible or not. If you look into the life history of the individuals who have these persistent psychoses, it's interesting to find that there is almost always another member of their family, usually one parent, who is psychotic. It makes you wonder whether LSD alone is responsible.

A member of the audience: I'd like to ask these two gentlemen if they have involved themselves in the personal research of the drug, the taking of LSD or of other psychedelic drugs. And if so, did they derive any particular value out of their experience? If not, do they feel that such an action as taking drugs would in any way limit their ability to perform as impartial observers of the events?

The moderator: The question to the panel members is have they taken the drug? I find this question one of the silliest nuisances in student discussions about LSD. I thought that when people were freshman they spent a lot of time pondering on how we come to know about things and that one of the first things they began to learn is that we come to know about things by many methods other than personal subjective experience, indeed, that most of these other methods are more important to us. I will let the panel deal with this particular side issue. Do you care to comment on it?

Dr. Jarvik: I agree with Mr. Leaf. I don't think that the personal experience of an investigator necessarily influences his research; however, I do admit that I have taken LSD a couple of times a long time ago. I must add, though, that at the time I took it, which was in the early fifties, I didn't get any of the transcendental effects that seem to be so common nowadays. I was in the wrong atmosphere, of course.

Mr. Giarman: I took the drug inadvertently one time by using a little probe with which we weigh out material to open another bottle, to get through the plastic wrapper. I injected myself with the probe, which had some LSD on it, getting a subcutaneous dose. It wasn't very much, but I immediately called my friend and colleague Dr. Freedman, a psychiatrist, and said, "Now, if I begin to act strange, I want you to take over." He said, "How am I going to tell the difference?" The important point here was that the whole episode was so disturbing to me, because I wasn't prepared for this experience. I didn't particularly want it, and I was quite depressed about it. I think really that my major reaction to this was a depression of greater proportions than is usually experienced. I have heard since, from my psychiatrist-colleagues, that people who are prone to depression generally respond to LSD with further depression, in spite of the fact that pharmacologically it is a central stimulant. But there was one aspect of the question that I think important, that is, that I have observed many people who had taken LSD, and I think that the best kind of research on this can only be done if the observer is qualified to observe and has not had the drug at that time.

Dr. Purpura: We forget the fact that Hofmann was, fortunately, such an objective scientist, not a psychiatrist; and in a way, this is why we are here today talking about LSD. Had this man not had the insight as an objective and carefully trained scientist, he might not have realized that what was happening to him was an experience over and above anything that he himself understood. If he had had a serious problem in the past, like the problems that everybody had in 1943, and had experienced this without the acumen to realize that it was something strange to him, I am certain that he might have institutionalized himself or gone to someone and said, "I've had it. Lock me up. I don't know what I'm going to do next." His objectivity, you see, was very important. I think that you don't have to play the organ like E. Power Biggs to appreciate a Bach fugue. Consequently, I don't think that the scientist has necessarily to have involved himself in the taking of the drug to appreciate its effects and to work on it. So that when you asked the question, I thought it totally irrelevant in terms of whether or not any of us has, at any one time, taken the drug. It would not color our experience.

The moderator: By the way, a majority of the panel have taken the drug.

A member of the audience: What is the relationship of LSD to alcohol?

Mr. Giarman: I can't answer the question about the inter-action of LSD and alcohol. Perhaps Dr. Jarvik knows the answer to this. I was going to ask Dr. Jarvik, because he did mention a number of other interactions, if the interaction of LSD with reserpine has been studied.

Dr. Jarvik: I honestly don't know the answer to the alcohol-interaction question myself. Dr. Kurland, I suspect, is going to tell us something about this this afternoon, when he tells us about the use of LSD in the treatment of alcoholics. LSD is clearly one of a different class of drugs. Alcohol is a sedative-hypnotic and has cross-tolerance with other sedative-hypnotics, but not with LSD. I don't know the answer to the question about reserpine; but you pointed out yourself that reserpine apparently can potentiate the action of LSD, perhaps by depleting amines.

Mr. Giarman: Well, one of the reasons that I was interested in this interaction was that Dr. Purpura showed this profound LSD effect on the reticular and the limbic systems of the brain, and it's known that LSD and reserpine have similar effects here and also in the reticular-activating system. I wonder, from a psychological point of view, whether they are similar in any way?

Dr. Jarvik: Whether they would interact?

Mr. Giarman: Whether they are similar in terms of the experience that they produce.

Dr. Jarvik: Taken singly, they produce very, very different effects, just the opposite, perhaps. Maybe the reserpine-induced depression has something to do with LSD-induced depression, which sometimes occurs.

A member of the audience: Some of the panel could talk about tolerance to LSD. It is my understanding that if there's any tolerance, it is of very short duration and that actually after a period of a week or two there is no remaining tolerance. I wonder if there is any comment on this, as it is not in any way the kind of tolerance that would develop to narcotics. I think there's a point to be made clear about the sensation as well.

Dr. Jarvik: Well, I can answer that, in part at least. I know that in monkeys we found both kinds of tolerance. We found tolerance lasting a few days and also residual tolerance, which lasted for months. We never got an effect that was as strong as we did the first time we gave the drug to an animal. Maybe this is similar to the long-lasting tolerance that one sees with narcotics. In humans, by and large, after a week or two most of the tolerance has disappeared, and you can achieve a fairly reproducible effect.

The moderator: You can get a very high tolerance, can't you?

Dr. Jarvik: You get amazingly high tolerance with LSD. As Mr. Giarman indicated, the effects on the second day are practically nil with 100 μg of LSD in some individuals. There is marked variability, too, in the development of tolerance, and I should add that there is marked variability in susceptibility to LSD. We have had individuals who have gotten as high as 225 μg of LSD without any effects. It was like giving them water. What the reason is for the individual differences I don't know.

Mr. Giarman: Is it true, Dr. Jarvik, that schizophrenics are more resistant to the actions of LSD?

Dr. Jarvik: I doubt it. The literature is controversial on this, and it depends upon the kind of measurement taken, whether it is anecdotal or quantifiable. If you use a quantifiable measure, you really can't find any difference. It's hard to say, because you start with a different base line. Schizophrenics are already psychotic to begin with, so you are trying to study a change in state. I might add that this question of individual differences is probably related to the prominence of LSD today. Dr. Hofmann appears to have been one of those individuals who are exceedingly sensitive to the drug. After he experimented with it for a while, he induced his colleagues Rothlin and Stoll to take it. Rothlin got no effects whatsoever. But, luckily, by that time it had been given out to Dr. Stoll's son, a psychiatrist, and he had given it to large numbers of people, and it was obvious that it was having a true pharmacological effect.

A member of the audience: Do you feel that the effect that LSD has on the biogenic amines is significant in the depressed patient? Is this the reason that you get a more severe reaction with LSD? You said the monoamine oxidase inhibitors would increase the amines, at least in the treatment of some of the patients.

Mr. Giarman: One of the highly speculative theories about affective disorders and depression concerns the catecholamines. Depression is thought to be caused by a relative deficiency in the general vicinity of the receptors of catecholamines. It's possible that this is why you get a potentiation of the LSD effect following reserpine treatment. There's no question that this happens, both in men and in animals. It's well documented.

A member of the audience: I should like very, very much to hear a little more about the influence of the drug LSD on the sense of time.

The moderator: Yes. Dr. Jarvik, would you comment further on the influence of the drugs on the sense of time.

Dr. Jarvik: There are a number of studies that have been made, but the essence of them seems to be that only the variability in estimating time is increased with LSD, not a prolongation, nor a shortening of the subjective sense of time. That's if you take a large group of subjects, as it is possible that in a single subject you may get one who shows consistent changes.

The moderator: A member of the audience asked a question about the specificity of effects of LSD. Dr. Jarvik expressed some explicit and some implicit skepticism about the uniqueness of many of the reported effects of LSD.

Dr. Jarvik: These are both interesting questions. The problem with complex behavior is that it involves a hierarchy of functions with each function depending upon the other. Sometimes it is difficult to disentangle one from the other. I myself raised the point that motivation might possibly be responsible for an impairment in intellectual functions. One of the experiments that we did with monkeys was to see whether LSD would impair the way they work on a delayed-alternation task, to get water. There was some depression of rate in the situation as well as of accuracy. But we found that with amphetamine, for example, we would get a marked depression of rate without any depression of accuracy, which would indicate, at least in this case, that it was thirst that was responsible, yet not solely responsible, because you could decrease the water-getting habits of the animal without influencing its accuracy. You always have to use indirect approaches to get at this problem. With respect to the question of tolerance, I think there's enough evidence to indicate that the tolerance to LSD is physiological, because Isbell has studied tolerance in a variety of ways. He has put subjects into task-performing situations and found that the performance of the task improves with subsequent administrations of LSD. But he has also found that if he doesn't make them perform, but simply gives the LSD beforehand, the first time they had to perform after they had been given LSD a number of times, the drug had very little effect. The situational factor can be examined in this way. You can't ever tell for sure whether the initial experience has something unique about it that is above and beyond the action of LSD on the chemical receptors, whatever they might be, which might be responsible for tolerance.

The moderator: The question for Dr. Jarvik is whether or not there are sensitization mechanisms as well as tolerance.

Dr. Jarvik: I think that what the questioner wants to find out is whether, as one of my colleagues once told me, making a journey or taking a trip is facilitated by subsequent experiences with LSD. Of course, you have here very strong psychological influences, so that even if you had the development of some kind of pharmacological tolerance, an individual who comes to these sessions becomes accustomed to them or learns what he is supposed to do with repeated experiences. They might very well learn it without the drug also. Perhaps sensitization refers to a learning experience. I don't know precisely what you were asking there.

What was the second question?

The Moderator: The second question had to do with brain damage.

Mr. Giarman: As a matter of fact, I introduced into my talk from one of the early reviews a statement that in dogs brain damage had been found. It is referred to in an article by some Italian scientist in an obscure Italian journal. Just yesterday I got hold of, the journal and found that not only was there brain damage in the dog, but there was also damage in the liver and in the kidneys. I was not at all surprised because the man was giving 500 μg/kg, which is a lot bigger than that dose that killed the elephant. I don't know of any evidence for brain damage in the human, and I suppose it's a little early for the LSD aficianados to come to autopsy, so we'll have to wait.

Dr. Jarvik: It's an important question, of course, whether the drug can cause brain damage or not; but it's a question that's almost impossible to answer. It is almost impossible to answer even with a commonly used drug like alcohol. If you get your information from the W.C.T.U., there's no question that alcohol causes brain damage; but if a whiskey manufacturer tells you about it, the chances are that it doesn't. I suspect that if you gave 500 μg/kg or larger doses to a human being and could keep him alive, you might get brain damage. Certainly if you got spasm of the arteries in the brain for a long enough period of time, localized gangrene would develop, or if you got spasm of the carotid or another artery, you might get damage. But I doubt that LSD will do it.

Dr. Purpura: Let me say just a word. When you talk about brain damage, we haven't nowadays even the vaguest idea of what is meant by it. We are in a phase of molecular biology in medicine, and what is damage in the sense of what happens to a cell under the microscope, even the electron-microscope, doesn't mean a thing today. If we're really thinking about changes that occur at transactions between macromolecular species that are altered—and this alteration can affect the membrane properties of another neuron— then "damage" in the normal physiological operation of the synapse has occurred, without the necessity for a detectable, old-fashioned view of what brain damage is. I think that this has been our whole problem in even trying to classify brain damage in psychotic behavior when there's no other known factor. And I think that we are moving into an area where refinements of analysis of what is the meaning of brain damage are occurring. I wouldn't be a bit surprised if eventually such raw, good objective information will be available, but it's going to take many more years.

A member of the audience: One of the major reasons why people are concerned with LSD is that they call it a consciousness-expanding drug, and they feel that they get insights into the way the world really is when they take it. I was wondering if you would speculate on why people might get this feeling when they take the drug and whether they were being fooled, or whether there was some reason why LSD could let down certain inhibitions, so that they might be able to see through institutions. Is it because a more conditioned way of looking at institutions is suppressed by the drug, and they are therefore able to see things in a more accurate way? I just wondered if you could speak to that.

The moderator: Dr. Jarvik, would you like to try? And to list the problems of control?

Dr. Jarvik: I don't think that I shall now. I would like to say that in the days before psychoanalysis, it was very popular for a doctor to tell his patients to take a vacation somewhere if they weren't feeling well, particularly if they were wealthy. Sometimes the patients felt that they benefited from this. They went to a spa somewhere, and there was a change of scene. It would be very difficult to document the real value of changing environment, but it's certain that taking LSD is a novel experience for an individual. It produces sensations that they have not yet, by and large, had before, unless they have taken marijuana or mescaline or some other drug. It becomes a sort of philosophical question in a way, but I think that the problem of what factors are involved in creativity might enter in here. Mr. Barron is going to tell us something about that later.

The moderator: You will learn some more about these things, I think, later this afternoon. As far as today's topic is concerned, the problem of experimental control and the factoring out of this kind of thing is not very well understood with LSD; but again, if I may recall some history for you, there have been controversies about hypnosis, for example, the problem of what this subjective experience is like and what is unique in it, for several hundred years. These controversies are still not resolved, and there are still many skeptical people, who on the basis of careful, controlled experiments are unwilling to believe that there are any properties unique to the hypnotic experience. The problem of suggestibility and placebo response, essentially, is enormous with any of these drugs. The problem, for example, of sensitivity may be like that problem with marijuana. I think that experienced marijuana users more easily think that they are smoking marijuana when, in fact, they are smoking oregano or orange-pekoe tea than inexperienced marijuana users. I presume that their previous experience has something to do with that. But that's common opinion, at least among people who sell things alleged to be marijuana.

Notes on Contributors

FRANK BARRON (B.A. LaSalle College, Ph.D. University of California) is a research psychologist of the Institute of Personality Assessment and Research of the University of California in Berkeley. A recognized authority on the psychological aspects of human creativity, Mr. Barron is the author of *Creativity and Psychological Health* (1963), among other books, and has contributed numerous articles to professional journals. He has lectured at several American colleges and universities and has recently been awarded a Guggenheim Fellowship for cross-cultural research in Italy.

NEIL L. CHAYET (B.A. Tufts University, LL.B. Harvard University) is an assistant professor of legal medicine at the Law-Medicine Institute of Boston University as well as a practicing lawyer. He is the author of a number of books and professional articles on problems of medical jurisprudence and is currently a member of the drafting committee for recodification of the Massachusetts laws of mental health.

RICHARD C. DEBOLD (B.A. University of California, M.S. Yale University, Ph.D. University of California) is Dean of Students and an associate professor of psychology at Hobart College and a recognized expert on the physiological basis of learned behavior. Mr. DeBold is currently preparing both a manual of experiments and a college textbook of psychology.

NICHOLAS J. GIARMAN (A.B. New York State Teachers' College, Ph.D. Yale University) is a professor of pharmacology at the Medical School of Yale University, where he has been a member of the faculty for eighteen years. Mr. Giarman is an active researcher and has published nearly one hundred articles, one of which is now considered the definitive review of the pharmacology of LSD.

MURRAY E. JARVIK (B.S. City College of New York, M.A. University of California at Los Angeles, M.D., Ph.D. University of California) is an associate professor of pharmacology at the Albert Einstein College of Medicine and the president of the Division of Psychopharmacology of the American Psychological Association. Dr. Jarvik has studied the effects of LSD on behavior intensively and is recognized as one of the most knowledgeable researchers in this area. He has written over seventy articles about his work for professional journals and is himself the managing editor of *Psychopharmacologia*.

MILTON H. JOFFE (A.B., M.S. University of Rochester, Ph.D. Ohio State University) has been associated for over twenty years with various research projects of the federal government, such as the Wright Field Aeromedical Laboratory and the Hanford Atomic-Energy Installation. Mr. Joffe is now a member of the Division of Drug Studies and Statistics of the Bureau of Drug Abuse Control of the Food and Drug Administration.

ALBERT A. KURLAND (B.S., M.D. University of Maryland) has been the Director of Research of the Maryland State Department of Mental Hygiene since 1960, in which capacity he directs the largest currently operating investigation of the therapeutic potential of LSD at the Spring Grove State Hospital in Baltimore. Dr. Kurland and his associates have published over one hundred articles on psychiatry and psychopharmacology.

RUSSELL C. LEAF (A.B. University of Chicago, Sc.M. Brown University, Ph.D. University of Pennsylvania) is an assistant professor of psychology and biology at Wesleyan University and an active researcher in psychopharmacology. Mr. Leaf was from 1963 until 1966 the senior research psychopharmacologist of the Squibb Institute for Medical Research.

DONALD B. LOURIA (B.S., M.D. Harvard University) is an associate professor of medicine at the Cornell Medical College and the head of the Infectious Disease Laboratory of Bellevue Hospital in New York City. Dr. Louria has been very active in work on the social problems of narcotics as the chairman both of the

Subcommittee on Narcotics and of the Public Health Committee of the New York County Medical Society and as president and member of the New York State Council on Drug Addiction. In 1966 he was MacArthur Lecturer at the University of Edinburgh and is currently the Lowell Lecturer at Harvard University.

WALTER N. PAHNKE (A.B. Carleton College, M.D., S.T.B., Ph.D. Harvard University) is a teaching fellow of the Harvard Medical School and a resident in psychiatry of the Massachusetts Mental Health Center in Boston. Dr. Pahnke is currently on leave to carry out research on the therapeutic use of LSD with alcoholics, neurotics and terminal-cancer patients at the Spring Grove State Hospital in Baltimore. He has done extensive psychopharmacological research on LSD and similar psychotropic drugs both here and at the University of Göttingen. He is probably best known for his carefully controlled experiments concerning the effects of these drugs on mystical and religious experiences.

DOMINICK P. PURPURA (A.B. Columbia College, M.D. Harvard University) is now professor of anatomy and chairman of the Department of Anatomy of the Albert Einstein College of Medicine. From 1956 until 1966 Dr. Purpura was a member of the faculty of the College of Physicians and Surgeons of Columbia University. He is an eminent neuroanatomist and the recipient of numerous awards and fellowships. He has written many articles on neurophysiology and neuroanatomy and has for several years done extensive research on the synaptic effects of LSD.